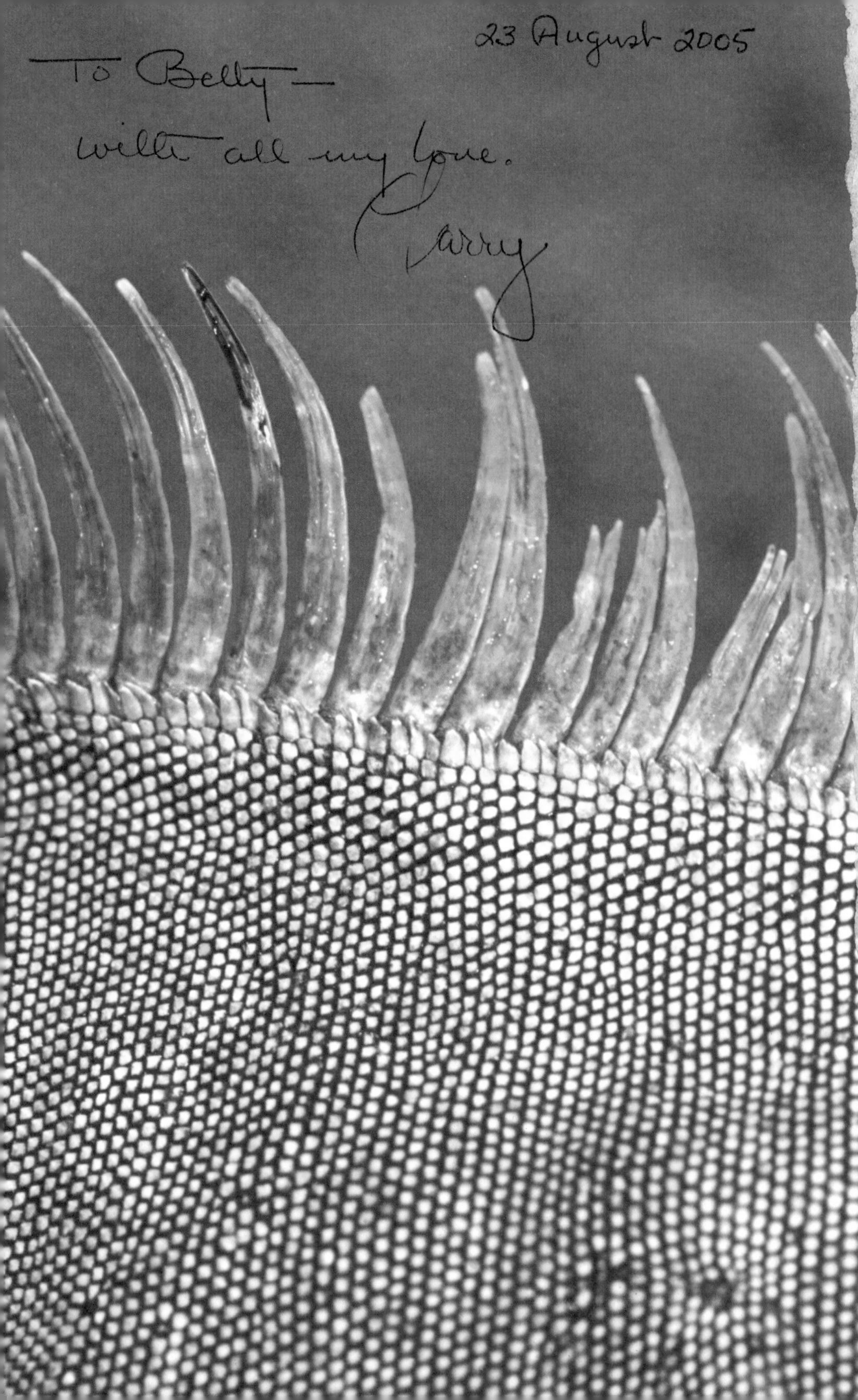

23 August 2005

To Betty —
with all my love.

Larry

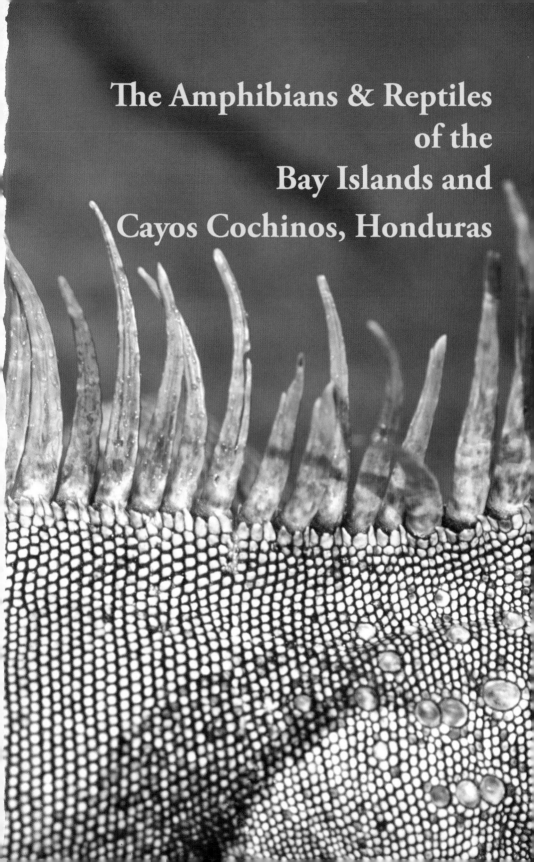

The Amphibians & Reptiles
of the
Bay Islands and
Cayos Cochinos, Honduras

The Amphibians & Reptiles of the Bay Islands and Cayos Cochinos, Honduras

James R. McCranie
10770 SW 164th Street
Miami, Florida 33157–2933, USA
e-mail: jmccrani@bellsouth.net

Larry David Wilson
Department of Biology
Miami-Dade College
Kendall Campus
Miami, Florida 33176–3393, USA
e-mail: lwilson@mdc.edu

Gunther Köhler
Sektion Herpetologie
Forschungsinstitut und Naturmuseum Senckenberg
Senckenberganlage 25
D-60325 Frankfurt am Main, Germany
e-mail: gkoehler@senckenberg.de

Bibliomania!

Published by: Bibliomania!, P.O. Box 58355, Salt Lake City, UT 84158, USA.
               Email: Breck@herplit.com; Internet: Herplit.com

ISBN: 1-932871-07-1

Printed in Singapore

The paper used in this publication meets the minimum requirements for the American National standard for Information Sciences—Permanence of Paper for Printed Library Materials. ANSI Z39.48-1992.

DEDICATION

We dedicate this book to the kind and generous people of the Islas de la Bahía, who over the years have shown us what "the island life" is all about. These wonderful people have made this book possible.

Larry David Wilson dedicates this book to the members of his Honduran family in Trujillo. These relatives of his wife, Elizabeth, have shown him many kindnesses over the 37 years since he first set foot in that historical town, the oldest permanent settlement on the mainland of the Western Hemisphere. Foremost among these people is his mother-in-law, Dolly Stephen, who holds forth from her porch on the "main drag" of the town, the same porch where Wilson first met his wife of 36 years. In addition, his sister-in-law, Daisy de Crespo and her husband, Oscar Crespo, have treated Wilson like a member of the family since he first met them in 1970. Finally, he thanks another sister-in-law, Hilda de Kolker, who opened her home to Wilson during time spent in Trujillo, most memorably in the summer of 2002. To all of them, *un abrazo fuerte.* It is also time to acknowledge the pleasure given Wilson by his canine companion of the last 12 years, Midnight. She showed up to help him cope during the dark days after Hurricane Andrew and, fortunately, never left.

Cnemidophorus lemniscatus, Isla de Roatán.
Photograph by Breck Bartholomew

Basiliscus vittatus, Isla de Utila
Photograh by Joe Burgess

CONTENTS

Iguana iguana, Isla de Roatán
Photograph by Breck Bartholomew

FOREWORD

The Honduras of most imaginations is one of a banana republic caught up in the political intrigues that have plagued Central America since the arrival of Europeans over 500 years ago. Christopher Columbus first sighted the Spanish Main here; Hernan Cortes established the oldest existing European mainland settlement here; and William Walker, delusional American filibuster, met his well-deserved demise here. But there is another Honduras with an equally colorful and tragic history that is anchored offshore in the clear, warm waters of the Caribbean.

The Bay Islands proper, consisting of three large islands and a scattering of smaller islets, and the smaller Cayos Cochinos group, are situated between 15 and 50 kilometers north of mainland Honduras. This relatively minor geographical distance, however, belies a significant difference in the cultural history of the two places. Mainland Honduras is typically Spanish Central American, while the islands, despite increasing encroachment of mainland influence, maintain an unmistakable Caribbean ambience.

My introduction to the Bay Islands was on July 14, 1967, when Larry Wilson, Terry Meyer, and I arrived by air at the exotic-sounding town of Coxen Hole on Roatán Island. Larry and I had first met in June of that summer to collaborate on fieldwork while I carried out my doctoral research on the Honduran herpetofauna. This proved to be the start of a long personal and professional relationship between us, and thankfully Larry continued to explore the herpetofaunal wonders of the country long after I moved on to other endeavors.

My first thought when approached by Larry to pen this foreword was, 'when do these guys find time to sleep?' By now, all serious students of Middle American herps are familiar with Randy McCranie and Wilson's monumental opus on Honduran amphibians, and the third author, Gunther Köhler, has been busy coaxing herpetological secrets from the islands. It is particularly gratifying to me to see these three authors collaborate on this exhaustive treatment of an island herpetofauna that I initially attempted to understand 35 years ago.

This book represents an exhaustive compilation of the three authors' labors in Honduran herpetology over the past three to four decades, and as such puts them in the unique position of being able to evaluate the islands' herpetofauna based upon their understanding of the regional fauna. As would be expected, the islands exhibit a reduced herpetofauna with respect to the mainland, 55 species versus 325 species, but surprisingly exhibit a similar degree of endemism, roughly 22 percent. Endemism is especially rich among the lizards and snakes, as opposed to the mainland, where a rich amphibian fauna contributes to a greater degree to the phenomenon. For me, having last explored the islands in 1967, it is a pleasure to see such a detailed presentation and analysis emerge at this distant date.

Of much lesser joy is to read these authors' evaluation of the status of the herpetofauna and the prognosis for the future. Fully nine manuscript pages have been devoted to a discussion of the problems facing Honduras, including the Bay Islands, most of which are a result of rampant population growth. Perhaps of equal importance as the authors' analysis of the herpetofauna is their thoughtful and in-depth discussion of the forces of human pressure now impinging upon this fauna. I know of no other publication of this nature that has gone so far in assessing this dilemma, and this alone makes it worth the price of the book. Readers should realize that the authors have successfully elucidated the likely future of all of Middle America as the overdeveloped countries continue, to their own ultimate detriment, to fail to meaningfully assist their economic colonies. Bravo to McCranie, Wilson, and Köhler.

John R. Meyer
Callahan, Florida
February 8, 2004

Coniophanes imperialis, Isla de Utila
Photograph by Breck Bartholomew

PREFACE AND ACKNOWLEDGMENTS

The Islas de la Bahía (the Bay Islands and Cayos Cochinos) traditionally have stood in marked contrast to the mainland of Honduras. They usually are placed as part of the "English-speaking Caribbean" (Stonich, 2000). This distinction is weakening, however, as the region becomes of more interest to the *ladino* mainland majority. English is still an important language, but Spanish has come to predominate on some of the islands, as the "Hispanicization" of the islands proceeds (Stonich, 2000).

We have been interested in the herpetofauna of these fascinating islands for some time, extending back 37 years in the case of Wilson. In fact, fieldwork conducted by Wilson, in the company of John R. Meyer in 1967 and Donald E. Hahn and Elizabeth Wilson in 1969 set the stage for an initial effort to understand the herpetofauna of the islands (L. Wilson and Hahn, 1973). Since those early years, we have traveled to the Bay Islands and Cayos Cochinos, sometimes singly, sometimes in pairs, to renew our interest in both the islands themselves and their herpetofauna. That interest, which led to the present book, has painted a considerably modified picture of the relationship of the herpetofauna to that of mainland Honduras since that presented by L. Wilson and Hahn (1973).

No scientific work is simply the work of its authors. The appearance of a book such as this one is preceded by several stages. All stages need to be accomplished or the book will not reach fruition, and each stage is accomplished only because of the assistance of other people.

The first stage involves fieldwork and resulting collections of specimens, the study of which forms the backbone of the book. The making of those collections required the issuance of scientific collecting permits from the responsible governmental agency. In our cases, working in Honduras, the issuing agency was COHDEFOR (Corporación Hondureña de Desarollo Forestal, Tegucigalpa), although in earlier years permits were issued by the Departamento de Recursos Naturales Renovables. For many years, Mario R. Espinal of Comayagüela, Honduras, acted as our agent by facilitating the acquisition of the necessary collecting permits. Since obtaining these permits typically takes several months, his on-site monitoring of this process was critical. In addition, while the Departamento de Recursos Naturales employed him, he issued several collecting permits. At COHDEFOR, Victor L. Archaga, Franklin E. Castañeda, T. L. Garcia, Leonel Marineros, A. P. Martínez, Martha Moreno, Hector Portillo, and A. M. Rodríguez were instrumental in supplying us collecting permits during our investigations into the herpetofauna of the Islas de la Bahía. Wilson's wife, Elizabeth, and his colleague at Miami-Dade College, Nidia Romer, have assisted with the Spanish translation of permit applications.

Once fieldwork was completed, specimens were catalogued into a major museum collection and given permanent identifying numbers. Most specimens we collected during our studies were deposited at the National Museum of Natural History (USNM) or Forschungsinstitut Naturmuseum Senckenberg (SMF). Steve W. Gotte curated the collections at the USNM and Köhler those at the SMF. See Materials and Methods for other sites of specimen deposition.

With the cataloguing completed, the writing began. This stage was the job of the three of us, but scientific writings always go through a peer review process, both before and after the final manuscript was submitted to the printer. We enlisted the aid of two colleagues, Jerry Johnson and Robert Powell, to review the manuscript prior to its submission to the printer. Their time consuming efforts to improve an earlier version of the manuscript are greatly appreciated.

Breck Bartholomew, John Binns, Joe Burgess, Cathi L. Campbell, Alexander Gutsche, Alan P. Jaslow, Paul M. Kornacker (Naturfoto-Kornacker), Mikael Lundberg, Louis W. Porras, Robert Powell, Alejandro Solórzano and Wayne Van Devender provided photographs and/or information on photographs that were considered for inclusion in this book.

During the writing phase of this project, Wilson was supported during a research leave at the University of Miami by funds from NIGMS (National Institute of General Medical Science) Grant No. 1R25GM0083–02 and HHMI (Howard Hughes Medical Institute) Grant No. 71195–14104. He is indebted to Michael S. Gaines and Robert L. Pope for providing that opportunity. In addition, the value of the research leave was increased tremendously by the assistance and collegiality provided by a long string of faculty and graduate students, who, among other things, helped deal with the pressure of spending long hours in a small room in front of a computer. Wilson is especially indebted to James O'Reilly, who opened his laboratory and provided him, among a long list of kindnesses, access to the Internet and a laser printer. Julian C. Lee, fellow student of the Middle American herpetofauna, assisted in many ways, from providing equipment and materials to the loan of literature. Dr. O'Reilly's Postdoctoral Associate, David Bickford, and his graduate student, Lisa Ganser, helped make the atmosphere in the laboratory warm and inviting. Miguel Fernandes, doctoral student of Dr. Gaines, provided friendship and discussions on a broad range of topics. Venetia Briggs, Dr. Lee's graduate student and native of Belize, provided warm smiles and happy hellos.

Over the years, we have been assisted in the field by a long string of friends and colleagues, including Breck Bartholomew, Gustavo A. Cruz Díaz, Alexander Gutsche, Donald E. Hahn, Elke Köhler, John R. Meyer, Kirsten E. Nicholson, John S. Parmerlee, Jr., Glenn Pederson, Günther Praedicow, Heinz Schuh, Robert Seipp, Jaime D. Villa, Elijah Welcome, and Elizabeth Wilson.

McCranie would also like to thank James "Jim" Bridges, Ed Casano, Louis W. Porras, and Robert Gerald "B.P." Prince for teaching him various techniques used in photographing amphibians and reptiles.

Finally, the printing company and its editorial personnel take over the job of turning a manuscript and its illustrations into a finished project. In this regard, our work was professionally transformed into this book by Breck Bartholomew, editor and owner of Bibliomania.

Cnemidophorus lemniscatus habitat, Isla de Utila. Photograph by Breck Bartholomew

Smilisca baudinii, Isla de Utila. Photograph by Gunther Köhler

INTRODUCTION

The purpose of this volume is to discuss the composition, distribution, natural history, biogeography, conservation status, and future of the herpetofauna of the Honduran department of Islas de la Bahía. We hope that this book will be of interest to residents of the islands, as well as the many tourists that go there to enjoy the splendid surroundings, and the "mainlanders" who want to learn something about the islands and their natural history. In addition, we hope that our fellow herpetologists and conservation biologists will find something of use in these pages.

The goal of our work is to increase the awareness of the people of the Bay Islands and Cayos Cochinos, and Honduras in general, to the ecological value of amphibians and reptiles in the upkeep of viable natural ecosystems in the American tropics. We also have been interested in increasing the understanding these people have of the composition of the herpetofauna of the area in which they live, the distribution of its members, and the means by which to identify them to species. Because amphibians and reptiles are not generally high on people's list of favorite animals, we also have sought to decrease the level of fear these creatures produce by increasing the knowledge of what these amphibians and reptiles are and are not capable of doing.

We also are interested in increasing the level of awareness and understanding of policymakers regarding the considerable biological value of the herpetofauna of the Bay Islands and Cayos Cochinos, as well as Honduras in general. Some policymakers live in Honduras, but others live in the United States, Europe, and other countries in Latin America. Only through the intervention of these decision makers can the natural habitats of the Islas de la Bahía have a future.

The fieldwork we undertook in preparing to write this book began in 1967, when Wilson and John (Jack) R. Meyer traveled to the Bay Islands, visiting Roatán and Guanaja. In 1969, Wilson again visited the Bay Islands, in the company of his wife, Elizabeth Pineda Wilson, and Donald E. Hahn, traveling to Utila, Roatán, and Guanaja, which resulted in a summary paper on the herpetofauna of these islands (L. Wilson and Hahn, 1973). Wilson again visited Roatán in 1976, during the academic year of 1975–1976 that he spent in Honduras. In 1988, accompanied by Gustavo A. Cruz Díaz and students from the Departamento de Biología of the Universidad Nacional Autónoma de Honduras, Wilson visited the Cayos Cochinos, resulting in a paper on the herpetofauna of that region (L. Wilson and Cruz Díaz, 1993). McCranie and Wilson visited Roatán in 1989 and McCranie returned to Roatán in 1989. McCranie, accompanied by John S. Parmerlee, Jr. and Jaime Villa, visited Guanaja, Barbareta, and Roatán in 1990. McCranie and Kirsten E. Nicholson visited Utila in 2001 and McCranie and Breck Bartholomew visited Roatán and Utila in 2004. Köhler visited Utila, Guanaja, and Roatán in 1994, Utila twice in 1995 and twice again in 1996, Utila and Guanaja in 1997, Utila and Roatán in 1998, and Utila three times in 1999, twice in 2000, and again in 2003. As a consequence of this fieldwork, we have collected on all of the major islands in the Bay Islands and the Cayos Cochinos to the point that we are reasonably assured that we have found the great majority of the members of the herpetofauna.

MATERIALS AND METHODS

The large majority of the amphibians and reptiles we examined in the preparation of this book came from our collections made since 1967. This material has been deposited in a number of museums including: Los Angeles County Museum of Natural History (LACM); Louisiana State University Museum of Science (LSUMZ) in Baton Rouge; Forschungsinstitut und Naturmuseum Senckenberg (SMF) in Frankfurt, Germany; National Museum of Natural History (USNM) in Washington, D.C. Additional material in other collections has also been utilized.

When we use the term "Las Islas de la Bahía," we are referring to the Honduran department that includes the Bay Islands and the Cayos Cochinos. When we use the term "the Bay Islands," we refer only to the island group including Barbareta, Guanaja, Morat, Roatán, and Utila.

Like all keys to identification, those presented herein have strengths and limitations. The principal strength is that they provide a relatively rapid means for tentative identification of a particular creature in hand. The keys will only identify organisms that are specifically covered in them, thus they will only identify species of amphibians and reptiles that are known to occur on the Islas de la Bahía. Also, an identification key constitutes only an initial step in the effort to place the correct scientific name on a given specimen. The next step in identification is to proceed to the species account for the species one thinks is in hand. If that description, which is obviously more detailed, fits, then the animal has probably been identified correctly. A final check can be made by examining the photographs provided, but the photographs are only of single specimens that were collected and photographed. Genetic variability is a fact easily ascertained by simply looking at other humans or examining the variation in a litter of puppies or kittens. Thus, the animal in hand may not exactly resemble the photograph in this book. Nonetheless, given these provisos, and after having gone through the three steps, one can be reasonably assured of a correct identification. The bottom line is that the keys presented herein will allow only a part of the identification process to be completed.

Conventions in the presentation of scientific name authorship are simple, but arcane. In general, the author's name follows the scientific name, which is composed of generic (the first capitalized) and specific (the second uncapitalized) portions, in turn followed by the date of first publication of the scientific name. The scientific name usually is italicized in print. As an example, the scientific name of the Boa, its authorship, and date of publication are presently rendered as *Boa constrictor* Linnaeus, 1758, signifying that this is the scientific name given to this snake by its original describer, Carolus Linnaeus, in his famous work Systema Naturae (see Literature Cited section), the 10th edition of which was published in 1758, and, in fact, constitutes the work from which all zoological nomenclature has its beginning. An indication of the importance of that work is given by noting that Linnaeus described seven of the 55 species covered in this book in 1758. When a given species has been transferred to a genus other than the one in which it was placed originally, the author's name and the date are placed in parentheses. For example, the scientific name of the Cane Toad, its authorship, and date of publication are given as *Bufo marinus* (Linnaeus, 1758), to indicate that the original generic name given to this species by Linnaeus (*Rana*) is different than the one in current use. Finally, when the date of publication for a scientific name is actually different from the date originally given, the incorrect date is placed in quotation marks and the correct date in parentheses (brackets if the generic name differs). Thus, the scientific name, its authorship, and date of publication of the leptodactylid frog *Leptodactylus melanonotus* is (Hallowell "1860" [1861]) to signify that the work in which this species was described actually appeared in 1861, not 1860, the date listed on the publication. In addition, Hallowell did not use the generic name *Leptodactylus* in his original description.

Common or vernacular names of amphibians and reptiles on the Islas de la Bahía generally arise from the local form of English used on these islands. Names are often colorful (from our standpoint) and describe some feature of structure or behavior of the creatures. We have listed those names and, in addition, have added Spanish vernacular names when we know that the names are associated with a particular species. Finally, for species not known to have an English common name on the Islas de la Bahía, we have used names given elsewhere in their ranges or have suggested one ourselves. In the former case, we have indicated the authority for the name and in the latter case an asterisk follows the suggested name.

The descriptions we provide are as untechnical as possible, while still giving a means to identify a given creature to species. In instances where words may be unfamiliar to the reader, one is directed to the glossary at the end of the book for explanations. In the snake descriptions, geographic range-wide variation in ventrals, subcaudals, and some other scales are given in parentheses immediately following the variation ranges for specimens from Honduras.

The section entitled "Similar species" provides a means to distinguish the species in question from those also known from the Islas de la Bahía that most closely resemble it. We have used, wherever possible, the distinguishing features that are easiest to observe.

In the statement of "General geographic distribution," elevational distribution is reduced to the following three categories: 1) low elevations are those found from sea level to 600 meters (m); 2) moderate elevations occur between 601 and 1500 m; and 3) intermediate elevations are those occurring between 1501 and 2700 m. Few elevations on mainland Honduras are above 2700 meters and no amphibian or reptile found in the Islas de la Bahía ranges at such elevations.

Distribution on the Islas de la Bahía is provided in terms of the islands on which the species have been found. Observations on habitat, microhabitat, and diel activity are indicated under "Natural history comments." The "Remarks" section of certain species accounts is used to identify a variety of other information of potential value or interest to the reader.

In the sections on ecological and biogeographic relationships, we used Duellman's (1990) Coefficient of Biogeographic Resemblance algorithm (CBR) for both types of relationships. The formula for this algorithm is CBR (or CHR for Coefficient of Habitat Resemblance) = $2C/(N1 + N2)$, where C is the number of species in common to both islands or habitat types, N1 is the number of species in the first island or habitat type, and N2 is the number of species in the second island or habitat type.

Many of the photographs that illustrate this work were taken either by Köhler or McCranie. In all cases, the photographer's name is indicated in the legends for these photographs. Most of the specimens used for the photographs came from the Islas de la Bahía, however, photographs of some specimens from other areas of Honduras (or occasionally other parts of Central America) were used when little or no distinction in general appearance from Islas de la Bahía animals exists.

DESCRIPTION OF THE BAY ISLANDS AND CAYOS COCHINOS

The following description of the Bay Islands and the Cayos Cochinos is based on our experience on all the major islands in these two island groups. In addition, we also have used information gleaned from published works on the area.

Physiography

The Honduran department of Islas de la Bahía comprises two major island areas, the Bay Islands and the Cayos Cochinos. The Bay Islands are the largest of the two groups, with a total land area of about 258 km² (Stonich, 2000). The Cayos Cochinos make up less than one percent of the land area of the department, at 2.28 km² in size.

The Bay Islands form a crescent in the waters of the Caribbean Sea off the north coast of the Central American country of Honduras (Map 1). The three largest islands, from west to east, are Isla de Utila, Isla de Roatán, and Isla de Guanaja. This island crescent also includes two smaller islands located off the eastern point of Roatán, Isla de Morat and Isla de Barbareta (Stonich, 2000). The eastern end of Roatán is sometimes considered a separate island, Isla de Santa Elena, but is, in fact, an extension of Roatán separated from the rest of

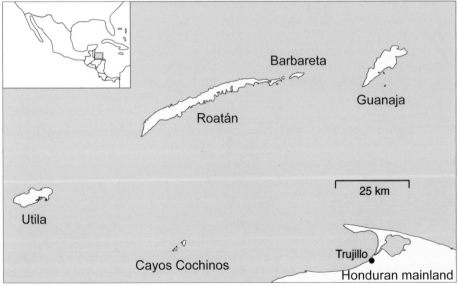

Map 1. Map of the Bay Islands and Cayos Cochinos showing their relationship to the Honduran mainland.

the island by a narrow mangrove-lined channel. Stonich (2000) also reported that the Bay Islands include 52 tiny keys or *cayos*, some of which are associated with each of the three major islands.

The Bay Island archipelago is part of the Middle American mountain complex that originates in the Sierra Madre de Chiapas in southern Mexico, continuing along the northwestern border between Guatemala and Honduras as the Sierra de Omoa, and departs the mainland near Puerto Cortés as the Bonacca Ridge, a submarine ridge that forms the southern edge of the Cayman Trough (Weyl, 1980). The Cayman Trough separates the North American and Caribbean Plates (Pinet, 1975). The Bay Islands are the only islands between the Central American mainland and Jamaica on which pre-Quaternary rocks are exposed (McBirney and Bass, 1969).

Isla de Utila differs from the remaining portion of the Bay Islands in that it lies on the continental shelf and is, therefore, a shallow-water continental island. The continental shelf surrounding Utila only reaches depths between 30 and 55 m and evidence suggests that this island was atop the exposed continental shelf and connected to the mainland during the Pleistocene from 13,000 to 18,000 years ago at the end of the Wisconsin glacial period. Roatán and Guanaja, in contrast, are oceanic islands surrounded by waters that reach depths of about 275 m. These two islands presumably were separated from the mainland, and each other, during the Pleistocene ice ages (see discussion and references in Villa and McCranie, 1995). Signs of volcanic activity during Holocene times are found only on Utila in the Bay Islands in the form of crater residues at Pumpkin Hill near its eastern end and scattered igneous rocks.

Relief and average elevation increase eastward on the Bay Islands, from the swamps of western Utila, through the low hills of eastern Utila and the higher hills of Roatán, to the relatively high, pine-covered ridges of Guanaja. The highest elevations on the three islands are 74 m, 235 m, and 415 m, respectively (L. Wilson and Hahn, 1973). Uplift of the portions of this island chain has not been regular, as several relatively low areas on eastern Roatán and southern Guanaja interrupt this general eastward rise.

The Cayos Cochinos constitute a small island group lying between the northern coast of the Honduran mainland and Isla de Roatán (Map 1). The group consist of two major islands, Cayo Cochino Grande and Cayo Cochino Pequeño, and a number of smaller keys.

Isla de Utila

Isla de Utila (Map 2) is the westernmost of the three major Bay Islands. It is also the smallest and lowest of the three and is closest to the mainland. Its greatest length and width are 12.7 km and 5.2 km, respectively (L. Wilson and Hahn, 1973), and its total area is 49.3 km². The island is largely flat, save for a rolling upland in the eastern portion, which averages about 12 m in elevation (L. Wilson and Hahn, 1973). Pumpkin Hill, near the northeastern end, at 74 m elevation, is the highest point on the island (L. Wilson and Hahn, 1973). Utila is divided into eastern and western portions by an artificial canal. The island lies about 32 km NNW of the port city of La Ceiba on the mainland.

Isla de Roatán

Isla de Roatán (Map 3) is the middle of the three major islands. It is also the largest

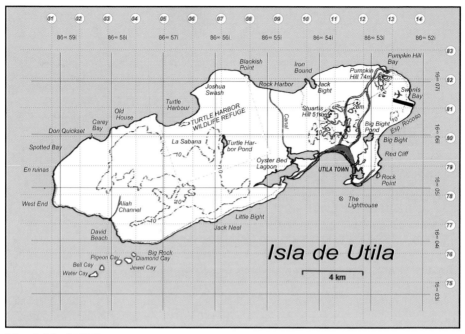

Map 2. Isla de Utila.

of the three, with an area of 155.9 km². It is long and narrow with greatest length and width of 48 km and 5.2 km, respectively. In contrast to Utila, most of Roatán lies at elevations above 20 m. The island's highest point is Picacho Hill (elevation 235 m), near the village of Oak Ridge. This hill is part of a range of hills stretching along the spine of the island. Roatán lies the farthest away from the mainland of any of the three major islands, and is about 48 km N of the mouth of the Río Papaloteca, between La Ceiba and Balfate (L. Wilson and Hahn, 1973). This island is about 30 km NNE of Utila and about 28 km W of Guanaja.

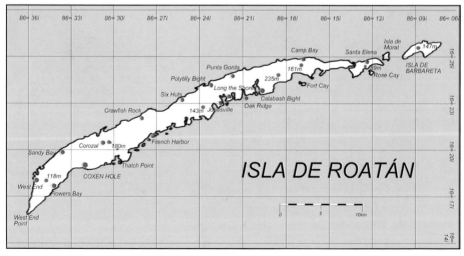

Map 3. Isla de Roatán.

Two small islands, Isla de Morat and Isla de Barbareta, lie a few km to the E of Roatán.

Isla de Guanaja

Isla de Guanaja (Map 4) is the easternmost of the three major islands. It has an area of 55.4 km² and is the most mountainous of the three islands. The highest point is Michael Rock Peak, at 415 m, which lies approximately in the middle of the island. The island is about 14 km long and about 6.2 km wide at its widest point (L. Wilson and Hahn, 1973). As with Roatán, most of Guanaja lies at elevations above 20 m and is located about 42 km N of Cabo de Honduras, near Trujillo.

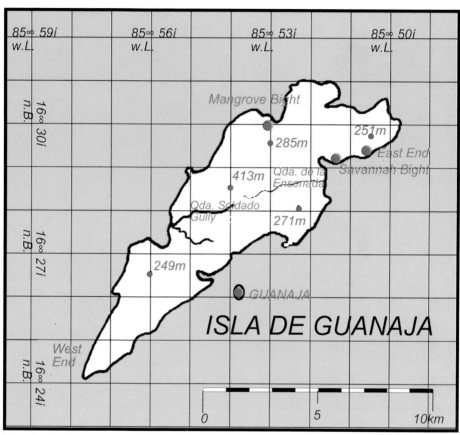

Map 4. Isla de Guanaja.

Cayos Cochinos

The Cayos Cochinos comprise the smallest portion of the Departamento de Islas de la Bahía under consideration herein (Map 5). They lie about 17 km N of Nueva Armenia, a village located at the mouth of the Río Papaloteca on the mainland. The two large islands, Cayo Cochino Grande and Cayo Cochino Pequeño, make up about 95% of the area of the island group (L. Wilson and Cruz Díaz, 1993). The larger of the two islands, Cayo Cochino

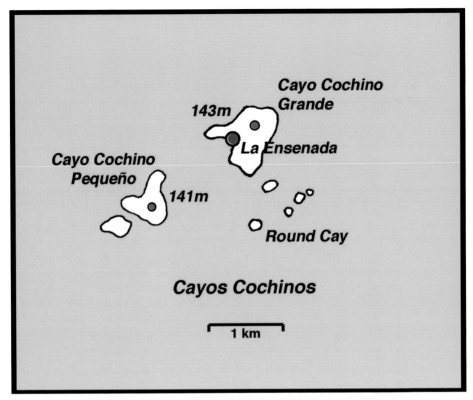

Map 5. The Cayos Cochinos.

Grande, has an area of 1.55 km². Seven keys totaling 9 ha or 0.09 km² are associated with this island (Davidson, 1974). The smaller of the two, Cayo Cochino Pequeño, has an area of 0.64 km². Six keys totaling 2.9 ha or 0.03 km² are located to the south and west of this island (L. Wilson and Cruz Díaz, 1993). Cayo Cochino Grande is a mostly hilly island, with

only 3.3% of the area being flat (Davidson, 1974). Cayo Cochino Pequeño is less hilly than the larger island, with about 7.7% flat land (Davidson, 1974).

Climate

Inasmuch as the Bay Islands and Cayos Cochinos are located within the American tropics at low elevations, the climate is warm and humid. Stonich (2000) reported that data gathered over a 38-year period from a meteorological station on Guanaja indicated an annual range of temperatures from 25 to 29°C and a mean of 27.5°C. The mean annual precipitation for the same period was 2571 mm, with less than 100 mm of precipitation generally falling each month from February through June, and the highest rainfall (46% of total annual precipitation) occurring during October and November.

Davidson (1974) presented additional rainfall data for the period of 1970–1978 recorded at Key Hole, Isla de Roatán. The mean annual precipitation for this period was 2162 mm, with 66.8% of mean annual precipitation falling from October through January. Davidson (1974:11) also noted, "The basically humid tropical climate of the islands shares with the nearby mainland [e.g., at La Ceiba; see L. Wilson and Meyer, 1985:7] a reversal from the characteristically wet summer of the tropics."

Stonich (2000:29) stated, "Because the islands lie in the trade wind belt, wind direction generally is from the east to southeast and wind velocity from 19 to 26 miles per hour. However, significant seasonal variation can occur. In August periods of up to 5 days of dead calm are common, while each winter about five North American cold fronts (*nortes*) reach the Bay of Honduras, bringing changes in wind direction to the north and west along with prolonged rainfall."

The Bay Islands and Cayos Cochinos are visited by hurricanes on an average of about once every ten years (Stonich, 2000). Hurricane Mitch, a devastating storm of category 5 strength, struck Honduras in late October 1998, and was the most recent in a string of about 20 storms that have affected the islands over the last 100 years (Stonich, 2000). The islands lie outside of the principal pathways of hurricanes, due to their northwestward and northward direction of travel, and are otherwise protected by the mountainous mainland of Honduras. However, these islands are occasionally struck by storms coming from the open

Undisturbed hardwood forest on Isla de Barbareta, 21 November 1989. Photograph by James R. McCranie

ocean, as was the case of Hurricane Francelia, in September 1969, and Hurricane Mitch (Stonich, 2000).

Habitats

In the Holdridge (1967) system of forest formations, the Bay Islands and Cayos Cochinos lie entirely within the Lowland Moist Forest formation. Within this broad classification, a number of identifiable habitats exist, although most of these have been heavily modified by human activity since the first record of logwood cutting on the Bay Islands in 1642 (Davidson, 1974).

Hardwood forests. L. Wilson and Cruz Díaz (1993:14) characterized the vegetation of the hills of Cayo Cochino Grande and Cayo Cochino Pequeño as "a relatively low, open, floristically simple type of tropical lowland rainforest," in which the dominant plants are encino (*Quercus oleoides*), a strangler fig (*Ficus* sp.), a cecropia (*Cecropia* sp.), and corozo palm (*Elaëis oleifera*). Hardwood forest also is widely distributed on Roatán and Barbareta, the eastern portion of Utila, and in several interior valleys and other low areas on the northern portion of Guanaja.

Pine forests. The pine forests of Roatán and Guanaja have been decimated by humans and nature. The dominant plant of these forests is Caribbean pine (*Pinus caribaea*), which has been harvested for centuries for use in mast building. As noted by Humphrey (2000:149), "What was left of the famed forest of Guanaja was utterly flattened by Mitch's 290-kph winds—the island's vegetation has only begun to recover."

Mangrove forests. Patches of mangrove forest, or *manglares*, are scattered along the shores of Roatán, Guanaja, Utila, and the Cayos Cochinos, as well as some interior portions of Utila (L. Wilson and Hahn, 1973; Davidson, 1974). L. Wilson and Cruz Díaz (1993) indicated that these forests were of limited extent on the Cayos Cochinos and that they consisted of Red Mangrove (*Rhizophora mangle*), Black Mangrove (*Avicennia germinans*), White Mangrove (*Laguncularia racemosa*), and Buttonwood (*Conocarpus erectus*).

Coconut groves and beach area vegetation. Coconut palms (*Cocos nucifera*) grow intermixed with other beach area vegetation on sandy beaches scattered intermittently on the Bay Islands and Cayos Cochinos and as the dominant plant on some small cays. A coconut palm plantation also was established formerly in the interior of Guanaja near Savannah Bight. This plantation was abandoned prior to 1967. Other coconut plantations occur in the interior of Roatán. L. Wilson and Cruz Díaz (1993:14), describing the situation on the

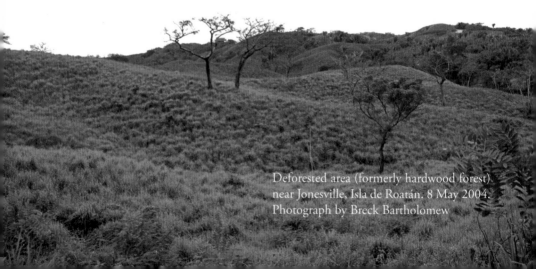

Deforested area (formerly hardwood forest) near Jonesville, Isla de Roatán. 8 May 2004. Photograph by Breck Bartholomew

Hardwood forest on Cayo Cochino Pequeño, 7
October 2001. A *Boa constrictor* lies on a branch
in the center of the photograph. Photograph by
Mikael Lundberg

Cayos Cochinos, stated "In some areas not maintained by [humans] a variety of other plants can be found. Near East End Village, for example, grows the beach morning glory (*Ipomoea pes-caprae*), wedelia (*Wedelia* sp.), seaside hibiscus (*Hibiscus tiliaceus*), and sand spurs. On the narrow isthmus back of Bonkes Nose Point, *Cocos nucifera* grows intermixed with gumbo-limbo or *indio desnudo* (*Bursera simaruba*), a thatch palm, buttonbush (*Conocarpus erectus*), sea grape (*Coccoloba uvifera*), and scattered tropical almond trees or *almendros* (*Terminalia catappa*)." However, Humphrey (2000:152) noted, "The Jamaica Tall coconut palms (*Cocos nucifera*) of the Bay Islands, normally a reliable source of liquid refreshment and shade, were struck in 1996 by Lethal Yellowing (LY), a mysterious plant disease responsible for the death of millions of palms in Florida, Jamaica, and Mexico. Despite programs to treat infested trees with antibiotics, the plague succeeded in wiping out most of the island's original trees. Early on when the disease hit, a few motivated islanders promoted replanting with LY resistant strains.... Many first-time visitors, seeing the new palms, will not know the difference." However, many dead coconut palms still can be seen on Utila, and the new palms are rather small.

Ironshore formations. At various sites along the shores of the Bay Islands and Cayo Cochinos are uplifted, fossilized fringing reefs locally called ironshore (Davidson, 1974; Humphrey, 2000). These exposed reef patches are full of cavities that provide refuge for lizard species of *Ctenosaura* (*C. melanosterna* on the Cayo Cochinos, *C. oedirhina* on Roatán).

Swamps and marshes. Swamps and marshes on the Bay Islands are low-lying areas that fill with stream overflows and excessive rainwater during the extended wet season. These habitats are known to occur on all three major islands on the Bay Islands, as well as on the eastern portion of Barbareta. All species of amphibians known to occur on the respective islands can be found in a single night during the rainy season at a swamp northeast of the town of Utila on the island of Utila and at a swamp near Savanna Bight on Guanaja.

Estuaries. The points where the relatively few streams on the Islas de la Bahía meet

Hardwood forest on Isla de Utila north of the town Utila, August 1997. Photograph by Gunther Köhler

Mangrove forest near Rock Harbor, Isla de Utila,
May 2004. Photograph by Breck Bartholomew

the ocean provide habitat for crocodiles and two species of turtles. Those estuaries are relatively small and limited in extent.

Marine environments. The marine waters surrounding the Islas de la Bahía support extensive reef systems, as well as flats that provide food sources for marine turtles. Sandy beaches provide potential sites for egg laying. Three species of marine turtles have been recorded from these waters.

Urban settings. As will be noted in the social history section, humans have occupied the Bay Islands for at least two and a half millennia. Their dwelling places have undoubtedly harbored some herpetofaunal species for much of that time. Currently, at least nine species share such dwelling places, including one toad and eight lizards.

SOCIAL HISTORY OF THE BAY ISLANDS AND CAYOS COCHINOS

The lengthy history of the human occupancy of the Islas de la Bahía began in pre-Columbian times, and the islands bear a sizable number of archaeological sites (Davidson, 1974). Who those pre-Columbian peoples were has been the subject of debate, with some concluding that they were related to the Pech (Humphrey, 2000) or the Paya (Stonich, 2000), both of which groups are represented today in eastern mainland Honduras. Others thought they were Maya (Sauer, 1966) or Lenca (Squier, 1855). Davidson (1974:19) stated, "However, there is information in the archeological, historical, and ethnographic records of the islands and adjacent mainland that suggests strongly the aboriginal islanders were Paya." Humphrey (2000:153), to the contrary, stated "Most archaeologists now agree, after years of dispute, that pre-Columbian islanders were related to the mainland Pech, who prior to conquest lived close to the coast near Trujillo." Whatever the precise identity of the aborigi-

Mangrove Forest, Isla de Utila.
Photograph by John Binns

nal inhabitants, they appear to have first set up full-time residency no earlier than A.D. 600 (Humphrey, 2000).

Davidson (1974) reported that innumerable sites exist on the Bay Islands from which modern islanders obtain "*yaba-ding-dings*" or artifacts for collection or sale. Archaeologists have classified these sites as residential, ceremonial, offertory, burial, and of unknown function (Davidson, 1974). Residential sites are identified by the presence of kitchen middens and abundant surface sherds, and range in size from about five to 40 acres (the latter is the so-called "80-Acre" site on Utila). Ceremonial sites, identified by the presence of large stone monoliths, earth and stone mounds, and stone causeways, have been found on Utila at Stuart's Hill and the Plan Grande site on eastern Guanaja (Davidson, 1974; Humphrey, 2000). Offertories, small votive sites without monuments, are almost always are found on hilltops, with the two largest on Barbareta and on central Roatán. These contain deliberately placed "offerings" of various types of artifacts. Three of eight known burial sites are located in a sand beach on Utila. Others are inland on isolated hilltops or in refuse heaps on all of the Bay Islands, except for Morat. Finally, a number of sites have been discovered that have no identifiable function (Davidson, 1974). The artifacts uncovered at these various sites suggest "… direct affinities between the Bay Islands and the mainland Paya area [located between Trujillo and the mouth of the Río Patuca], at least slightly before and during the early period of European contact" (Davidson, 1974:25).

The period of conquest and colonization of the Bay Islands by Europeans began with Columbus' landing on Guanaja in late July 1502 on his fourth voyage (Humphrey, 2000), although Davidson (1974:25) indicated "… there is evidence that Columbus was not the first European to visit the Bay Islands." Nonetheless, Columbus "… did pass through the islands on his fourth voyage (1502–1504) and provided the first known accounts of the area." Columbus named Guanaja "Isla de los Pinos" (Isle of Pines) based on the presence of impressive forests of *Pinus caribaea*, the same pine species found in the lowland pine savan-

Coconut palm habitat on Isla de Barbareta, 21 November 1989. Photograph by James R. McCranie

nas of the Mosquitia (L. Wilson and Meyer, 1985) and Belize (Stafford and Meyer, 2000). These pine forests are considerably less impressive these days, given that many were felled to make ship masts and for other purposes in earlier times and Hurricane Mitch largely flattened those that remained in 1998.

Uncontested Spanish rule over the Bay Islands continued for 136 years past the initial European contact (Davidson, 1974). The Bay Islanders "… were treated in much the same manner as other easily accessible Caribbean populations, first subjected to slave raids, later Christianized and used as a labor supply" (Davidson, 1974:31). In 1516, the first known incident of slave raiding occurred when Spaniards made off with 300 natives bound for Cuba. The natives, however, took over the ship near Cuba and sailed back to their homeland (Humphrey, 2000; Stonich, 2000). In the ensuing years, several other slaving expeditions resulted in the capture of other Bay Islanders for use in the mines of Cuba and "Española" (= Hispaniola). In 1530, the first *encomienda* (providing a conquistador rights to demand labor and tribute from locals, presumably in return for governance and religious education) was granted on the Bay Islands (Humphrey, 2000).

Soon after the establishment of the *encomienda*, European freebooters made their appearance, with French raiding boats arriving in 1536, followed by the English in 1564 (when a single English ship captured four Spanish frigates) and the Dutch in 1594 (Stonich, 2000). The English, however, were the most successful in disrupting Spanish control of the Caribbean region (Stonich, 2000). By the early 1640s, the persistent use of the Bay Islands as a base for pirate sorties and, for a period of time, as a settlement area for the British Providence Company, seriously undermined the authority of the Spanish, who decided to depopulate the islands, moving the indigenous peoples to the mainland where they could work to supply provisions for the Spanish fleet without the threat of the supplies being expropriated by British pirates (Humphrey, 2000; Stonich, 2000). Instead of decreasing the popularity of these islands for the British, however, the reverse occurred, leading to "enhanced British

Coconut palm habitat at Iron Bound, Isla de Utila, 20 April 2000. Photograph by Alexander Gutsche

Sea grape tree (*Coccoloba* sp.) in beach area vegetation near Santa Elena, Isla de Roatán, 21 November 1989. Photograph by James R. McCranie.

efforts to settle and politically control the islands" (Stonich, 2000:32).

The Bay Islands were so attractive to the buccaneers because the Gulf of Honduras was the only site of Spanish ports, at Trujillo and Puerto Caballos (= Puerto Cortés), between New Spain and Panamá. These two relatively indefensible ports were used to make ready for transport products from the interior of Honduras, including gold. In addition, the small harbors, especially those on the southern side of Roatán, made excellent refuges for the buccaneers for careening and refitting ships, cutting logwood, hunting wild hogs, fishing, and turtling (Davidson, 1974; Stonich, 2000).

The conflict between England and Spain intensified from 1638 to 1782 in the western Caribbean (Davidson, 1974). Declaration of war between England and Spain came in 1739 and British military occupation began in 1742, continuing for several years at Port Royal, on the southern side of Roatán, where two small forts (Fort George and Fort Frederick) and two small settlements were constructed, and at Sandy Bay, on the northern side (Humphrey, 2000; Stonich, 2000). In 1748, the Spanish were awarded the Bay Islands as part of the Treaty of Aix-la-Chapelle. The British force left in November 1749 and the last of the British settlers were removed in 1751 (Humphrey, 2000; Stonich, 2000). Another outbreak of war between England and Spain led to the return of the British to the Bay Islands in 1779. In 1782, however, the Spanish attacked Port Royal, destroying the forts and the surrounding town and captured 200 British soldiers and slaves, leaving Roatán uninhabited after sailing to Trujillo (Humphrey, 2000; Stonich, 2000).

The development of the modern Bay Islands began with the establishment of the Garífuna village at Punta Gorda on the northern coast of eastern Roatán. The 4000 Garífuna or Black Caribs marooned on the then-deserted island by the British on 12 April 1797 were the first people to form a settlement on the Bay Islands; their descendents remain to the present day (Davidson, 1974; Humphrey, 2000). These Garífuna were dissident prisoners from the island of St. Vincent (Stonich, 2000). The Spanish looked at this move as an attempt to

Beach area vegetation at Iron Bound, Isla de Utila. 20 April 2000. Photograph by Alexander Gutsche.

Ironshore formation near Flowers Bay, Isla de Roatán, 8 May 2004. Photograph by Breck Bartholomew

Temporary swampy area 1.3 km NNE of Utila (town) on road to Pumpkin Hill Beach, Isla de Utila, 24 September 2001. All five species of frogs known from Isla de Utila can be found here during the rainy season. Photograph by Alexander Gutsche

reoccupy the island by the British and sent forces to recapture the island. They attempted to remove the Garífuna to a settlement near Trujillo; most left, but a few remained, establishing the settlement of Punta Gorda.

Following the abolition of slavery on the Cayman Islands on 1 August 1834, waves of immigrants, both white and black, headed for the western Caribbean during the period of 1832–1850 (Davidson, 1974; Humphrey, 2000), with many ending up in Belize and the Bay Islands. The newcomers laid the foundations for the present-day towns. They first moved to a cay off Utila, then to Coxen Hole, Flowers Bay, and West End on Roatán and the Sheen and Hog Cays off eastern Guanaja, two cays that were eventually joined and expanded by landfilling, purported to have begun in about 1935, to make the present-day Bonacca Town (or Guanaja Town) (Davidson, 1974; Humphrey, 2000).

During the period of 1838–1852, England and Spain jockeyed for primacy on the Bay Islands, with the British interests supported by wealthy Belizean merchants, who feared the takeover of the islands by commercial rivals (Stonich, 2000). Even so, not until March 1852 were the Bay Islands formally declared a British colony. At this point, the United States of America entered the picture, claiming violation by England of the Monroe Doctrine and the Clayton-Bulwer Treaty, the latter agreement prohibiting the fortification, occupation, or colonization of any part of Central America by either nation (Stonich, 2000). By 1855, the United States formally charged England with violation of this treaty and, in 1859, Britain agreed to sign the Wyke-Cruz Treaty, which returned the Bay Islands to Honduras in 1861 (Stonich, 2000). In 1872, the Islas de la Bahía officially became a department of Honduras (Stonich, 2000).

Many islanders of this period, however, considered themselves to be part of the British Empire and sent Queen Victoria several petitions for reinstatement as a British colony, to no avail. Nonetheless, "many islanders maintained their assertions of British nationality" as recently as 1955 (Stonich, 2000:42), although both Britain and Honduras recognized

Marine environment at northeastern end of Isla de Roatán, 8

them as citizens of the latter country. When Wilson visited Roatán in 1967, many islanders clearly considered themselves to have little cultural or political connection to the mainland, being proud of their descent from lineages other than mainland *ladino*.

With the return of the Bay Islands to Honduras in the early 1860s, the modern Bay Island society began to take shape. The cultural landscape encountered by Wilson about a century later, however, gave evidence of having been formed by uneasy interactions between the native islanders and the Tegucigalpa-appointed officials put on the islands to develop closer relations with the mainland through Hispanization. From 1917 to 1919, Lt. Colonel Rafael Barahona served as governor of the Bay Islands. During that time, he outlawed English-language schools and allowed instruction only in Spanish (Davidson, 1974). Nonetheless, not until the latest phase of the Bay Islands' social history began to unfold in the early 1960s did a new threat to the attempts to maintain a British atmosphere emerge.

Despite initial attempts at commercial fruit growing in the late 19th century, the economy of the Bay Islands, up to the current era past 1960, has depended almost entirely on marine resources (Humphrey, 2000). Fishing for shrimp, lobster, and conch is still important, and some 400 commercial boats ply the waters from all three of the major Bay Islands. Shipbuilding, especially in Oak Ridge on the southern coast of Roatán, has had a small impact. Many island men also make a living from merchant sailoring or from working on cruise ships during the tourist season (Davidson, 1974; Humphrey, 2000; Stonich, 2000).

This low-key, maritime way of life began to change in the 1960s when tourists, especially from the United States and Europe, began to discover the Bay Islands and the real estate boom began (Humphrey, 2000). Humphrey (2000:155) reported, "Since the late 1980s, the pace [of tourism] has picked up dramatically. In 1990, an estimated 15,000 tourists came to the islands, by 1993 that number doubled to 30,000, and by 1996 it had doubled again." In recent years, visits to the islands for two days each week by cruise ships

Urban setting at French Harbor, Isla de Roatán, 8 May 2004. Photograph by Breck Bartholomew

produced a short-lived, but sizable impact on the traditional Bay Island way of life. Tourism and real estate development suffered a setback in the wake of Hurricane Mitch, but Humphrey (2000) predicted that the slump would not last.

The movement of tourist and real estate dollars into the Bay Island economy has attracted poor people from the mainland looking for a respite from the minimal existence provided by farming already-exhausted lands in western and southern Honduras. Humphrey (2000:155) noted, "The changes wrought by tourism have benefited many islanders immensely, and most now live off the trade in one way or another. Even before the tourist boom, islanders had always maintained a better standard of living than their mainland countrymen (still called Spaniards by the islanders). Consequently a steadily growing stream of Latino immigrants have come over to get a piece of the good life, a trend that is changing the face of the islands—a trend some islanders are not too happy about." The interaction among tourism, real estate speculation, and mainland transmigration is expected to continue, and its impact on the future of the herpetofauna is explored in the final section of this book.

Anolis allisoni, Isla de Roatán. Photograph by Breck Bartholomew

THE HERPETOFAUNA

The herpetofauna of the Bay Islands and Cayos Cochinos comprises 55 species (Table 1), including seven anurans (of 92 species recorded for Honduras or 7.6%), one crocodilian (of two species or 50.0%), five turtles (of 14 species, including five marine forms, or 35.7%), 23 lizards (of 88 species or 26.1%), and 19 snakes (of 120 species or 15.8%). The total number of species makes up 16.0% of the 344 species of amphibians and reptiles presently recorded from Honduras and its coastal waters, including the Islas del Cisne (McCranie, 2004; McCranie and Castañeda, 2004; McCranie and Wilson, 2002; McCranie et al., 2002, 2003a, 2003b, 2005; L. Wilson and McCranie, 2002; L. Wilson et al., 2003). Unlike mainland Honduras, no caecilians or salamanders occur on the Bay Islands or Cayos Cochinos.

Of the 55 species making up the herpetofauna of the Honduran department of Islas de la Bahía, 50 or 90.9% occur on the Bay Islands and 19 or 34.5% on the Cayos Cochinos. The 50 Bay Island species include all seven anurans known from both areas, the only crocodilian species, four turtles, 20 lizards, and 18 snakes (Table 2). The 19 species known from the Cayos Cochinos include two anurans, three turtles, eight lizards, and six snakes (Table 2).

Modern reviews of the herpetofauna of the Bay Islands and Cayos Cochinos are in L. Wilson and Hahn (1973) and L. Wilson and Cruz Díaz (1993), respectively. Subsequently, several new species of reptiles have been described from the Bay Islands and Cayos Cochinos by de Queiroz (1987; *Ctenosaura oedirhina*), Villa and McCranie (1995; *Oxybelis wilsoni*), Köhler (1996a; *Norops utilensis*), Köhler (1996b; *N. bicaorum*), Buckley and Axtell (1997; *Ctenosaura melanosterna*), McCranie and Köhler (1999; *Enulius bifoveatus, E. roatanensis*), and Köhler and McCranie (2001; *Norops roatanensis*). In addition, L. Wilson and

Table 1. Composition of the Herpetofauna of the Bay Islands and Cayos Cochinos of Honduras.

Group	Families	Genera	Species
Anurans	4	6	7
Crocodilians	1	1	1
Turtles	3	5	5
Lizards	8	14	23
Snakes	4	14	19
Totals	20	40	55

McCranie (1999) resurrected *Tantilla tritaeniata* from the synonymy of *T. taeniata*. Also, the following authors have added several species of reptiles to the Bay Island herpetofauna: Köhler (1996b; *Thecadactylus rapicauda* and *Coniophanes imperialis*), Köhler (1998a; *Coleonyx mitratus* and *Imantodes cenchoa*), Köhler (1998b; *Bufo marinus*), Lundberg (2000; *Hemidactylus frenatus*; also see Köhler, 2001), Lundberg (2002; *Sphenomorphus cherriei* and *Leptodeira septentrionalis*), and Gutsche (2003; *Enulius flavitorques*).

Ctenosaura similis, Isla de Utila.
Photograph by Breck Bartholomew

Table 2. Distribution of the amphibians and reptiles of the Bay Islands and Cayos Cochinos.

Species	Isla de Utila	Isla de Roatán	Isla de Barbareta	Isla de Guanaja	Cayo Cochino Grande	Cayo Cochino Pequeño	Totals
Bufo marinus	—	—	—	X[1]	—	—	1
Hyla microcephala	X	X	—	X	—	—	3
Scinax staufferi	X	—	—	X	—	—	2
Smilisca baudinii	X	X	X	X	—	X	5
Leptodactylus melanonotus	X	X	X	X	X	—	5
Rana berlandieri	X	X	—	—	—	—	2
Rana vaillanti	—	—	—	X	—	—	1
Crocodylus acutus	X	X	X[2]	—	—	—	3
Caretta caretta	X	—	—	X	—	—	2
Chelonia mydas	X	X[2]	—	—	—	—	2
Eretmochelys imbricata	X	—	—	X	—	X	3
Trachemys venusta	X	X	—	—	X	—	3
Kinosternon leucostomum	—	—	—	—	X	—	1
Coleonyx mitratus	X	—	—	—	—	—	1
Hemidactylus frenatus	X[1]	—	—	—	—	—	1
Phyllodactylus palmeus	X	X	X[2]	X	X	X[3]	6
Sphaerodactylus millepunctatus	X	X	X	X	—	—	4
Sphaerodactylus rosaurae	X	X	X	X	—	—	4
Thecadactylus rapicauda	X	—	—	—	—	—	1

Table 2 (continued). Distribution of the amphibians and reptiles of the Bay Islands and Cayos Cochinos.

Species	Isla de Utila	Isla de Roatán	Isla de Barbareta	Isla de Guanaja	Cayo Cochino Grande	Cayo Cochino Pequeño	Totals
Basiliscus vittatus	X	X	X	X	X^2	—	5
Ctenosaura bakeri	X	—	—	—	—	—	1
Ctenosaura melanosterna	—	—	—	—	X	X^3	2
Ctenosaura oedirhina	—	X	X	—	—	—	2
Ctenosaura similis	X	—	—	X	—	—	2
Iguana iguana	X	X	X^2	X	—	X^3	5
Anolis allisoni	—	X	X	X	X	X	5
Norops bicaorum	X	—	—	—	—	—	1
Norops lemurinus	—	—	—	—	X	X	2
Norops roatanensis	—	X	—	—	—	—	1
Norops sagrei	—	X	—	—	—	—	1
Norops sericeus	X	—	—	—	—	—	1
Norops utilensis	X	—	—	—	—	—	1
Mabuya unimarginata	X	X	—	X	—	—	3
Sphenomorphus cherriei	—	—	—	—	—	X^3	1
Gymnophthalmus speciosus	—	X	X	X	—	—	3
Cnemidophorus lemniscatus	X	X	—	—	—	X	3
Leptotyphlops goudotii	X	X	X	X	X	X	6
Boa constrictor	X	X	X^2	X	X	X	6

Species	Isla de Utila	Isla de Roatán	Isla de Barbareta	Isla de Guanaja	Cayo Cochino Grande	Cayo Cochino Pequeño	Totals
Coniophanes bipunctatus	—	X	—	—	—	—	1
Coniophanes imperialis	X	—	—	—	—	X	2
Dryadophis melanolomus	X	—	—	—	X	X	3
Drymarchon melanurus	X	X	—	X	—	—	3
Emulius bifoveatus	—	—	—	X	—	—	1
Emulius flavitorques	X³	—	—	—	—	—	1
Emulius roatanensis	—	X	—	—	—	—	1
Imantodes cenchoa	X	—	—	—	—	—	1
Leptodeira septentrionalis	—	—	—	—	—	X³	1
Leptophis mexicanus	X	—	—	—	—	—	1
Oxybelis aeneus	X	X	X	X	X	—	5
Oxybelis fulgidus	X	—	—	—	—	—	1
Oxybelis wilsoni	—	X	—	—	—	—	1
Pseudelaphe flavirufa	X	X	—	X	—	—	3
Tantilla tritaeniata	—	—	—	X	—	—	1
Tretanorhinus nigroluteus	X	X	—	X	—	—	3
Micrurus ruatanus	—	X	—	—	—	—	1
Totals (55)	37	29	14	25	12	14	—

Table 2 (continued). Distribution of the amphibians and reptiles of the Bay Islands and Cayos Cochinos.

[1] = introduced species [2] = sight record [3] = photographic record

Keys and Accounts of Taxa

The included keys allow identification of the members of the herpetofauna to species (note the provisos concerning these keys in Materials and Methods). Each of the 55 species-level taxa (i.e., groups of organisms recognized at the species level of classification) of the herpetofauna is treated in an account dealing with various aspects of its biology.

Key to the Classes Amphibia and Reptilia

1 A.   No epidermal scales present; skin with numerous mucus and/or poison glands, generally moist to the touch ....**Class Amphibia (p. 29)**

   B.   Epidermal scales present on at least a portion of the body; skin free of mucus and poison glands, generally dry to the touch .... **Class Reptilia (p. 51)**

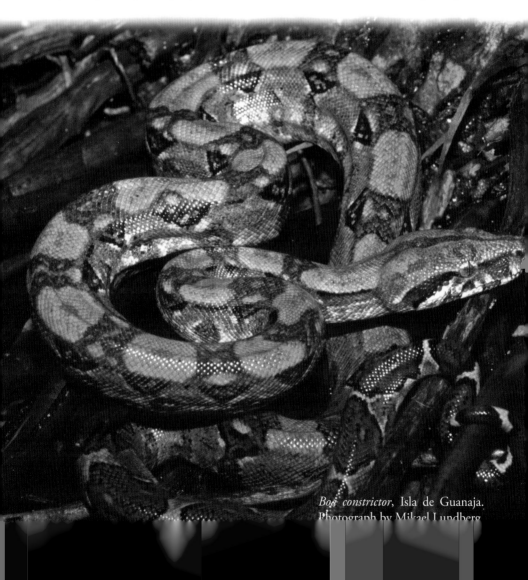

Boa constrictor, Isla de Guanaja. Photograph by Mikael Lundberg.

Class Amphibia (Amphibians)

The members of the class Amphibia, called amphibians, are one of the two groups of animals studied by herpetologists; the other group comprises the reptiles. Both of these groups belong to the tetrapod vertebrates, those animals possessing a vertebral column and lateral appendages adapted for locomotion on land (excepting amphisbaenians, most snakes, and some lizards in the case of lateral appendages). Amphibians represent a group transitional in the evolution of vertebrate life from water onto land. They are tetrapods, yet they are not amniotes. That is to say, as adults they can move about on land, but at least plesiomorphically, they have to return to water to reproduce. Thus, they possess a biphasic life cycle in many instances, in which the stage hatching from the egg is a larva, a non-sexual feeding stage, living typically in water, which then metamorphoses into an adult, by definition capable of reproduction, which typically lives on land. This is the type of life cycle practiced by all of the species of amphibians living on the Bay Islands and Cayos Cochinos.

Three orders of living amphibians exist (Pough et al., 2003). These orders comprise the caecilians (Order Gymnophiona), a group of legless, elongate, burrowing pantropical amphibians, the salamanders (Order Urodela), a group of tailed, quadrupedal largely cosmopolitan amphibians, and the anurans, or frogs and toads (Order Anura), a group of tailless, quadrupedal (with hind limbs modified for jumping or saltational mode of locomotion), largely cosmopolitan amphibians. Only members of the Order Anura occur on the Bay Islands and Cayos Cochinos, although representatives of all three groups are found on mainland Honduras. Seven anurans are recorded from the Bay Islands and two from the Cayos Cochinos (Table 2).

Order Anura (Frogs and Toads)

Anurans are poorly represented on the Islas de la Bahía, with only seven species, one of which is introduced (*Bufo marinus*). All seven are widespread and common on mainland Honduras (McCranie and Wilson, 2002). Anurans are amphibians that possess four limbs (Fig. 1). The hind limbs are larger than the forelimbs and are adapted for a jumping or saltational mode of locomotion. Adult anurans lack a tail, although the larval stages have one. Most frogs and toads have a larval stage, although some have direct development. In direct development, the young hatch from eggs as miniatures of the adults. The seven species occurring on the Bay Islands and Cayos Cochinos all have a larval stage and a generalized life cycle consisting of the laying of eggs in lentic (nonflowing water, such as temporary and permanent ponds, lakes, and swamps) or lotic (flowing water, such as streams and rivers) environments (McCranie and Wilson, 2002). Of the seven species, five (*Bufo marinus, Hyla microcephala, Scinax stauff), Smilisca baudinii,* and *Rana berlandieri*) lay their eggs in lentic settings. Their larvae feed in the same settings. Three species (*Bufo marinus, Rana berlandieri,* and *Rana vaillanti*) lay their eggs in lotic water (albeit slow-flowing), with their larvae feeding there as well. *Bufo marinus* and *Rana berlandieri*, thus, use both lentic and lotic environments for egg laying. *Leptodactylus melanonotus* departs somewhat from this generalized life cycle in that it constructs and lays its eggs in a foam nest in a temporary or permanent pond. Its tadpoles feed in the pond.

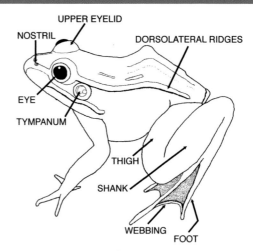

Figure 1. An adult frog showing general features. Modified from Fig. 3 in McCranie and Wilson (2002).

Key to the Species of Frogs and Toads of the Bay Islands and Cayos Cochinos

1 A. Conspicuous enlarged parotoid gland present posterior to each orbit (Fig. 2); cranial crests present dorsally (Fig. 2); maxillary, premaxillary, and vomerine teeth absent ....*Bufo marinus* (p. 34)

B. No enlarged parotoid gland present; cranial crests absent; maxillary, premaxillary, and vomerine teeth present (Fig. 3) 2

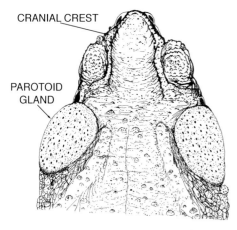

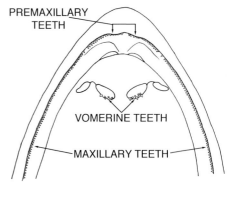

Figure 2. Dorsal view of head and forebody of *Bufo marinus* (SMF 81278) showing cranial crests and parotoid glands. Drawing by Linda Acker.

Figure 3. Ventral view of upper jaw of a frog (*Rana vaillanti*; SMF 77975) showing maxillary, premaxillary, and vomerine teeth. Drawing by Uta Imhoff.

2 A. No digital groove completely around tips of fingers and toes 3

  B. A small digital groove (Fig. 4) around tips of toes and at least Fingers III–IV, groove separating upper surface (disc covers) from subterminal disc pad (Fig. 4) 5

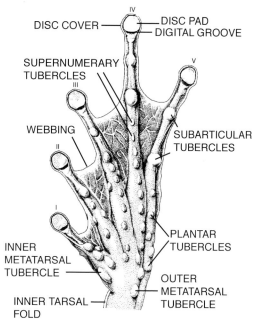

Figure 4. Ventral view of foot and distal portion of tarsus of a frog showing pertinent features used in identification of anurans. Modified from Fig. 3B in McCranie at al. (1993) and Fig. 10 in McCranie and Wilson (2002).

3 A. Toes with basal webbing or webbing absent; tongue not or only slightly notched posteriorly .... *Leptodactylus melanonotus* (**p. 44**)

  B. Toes with extensive webbing (Fig. 5); tongue deeply notched posteriorly (Fig. 6) .. 4

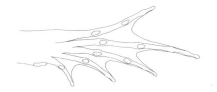

Figure 5. Ventral view of foot of *Rana berlandieri* (SMF 77991) showing extensive webbing and the toe tips not expanded. Drawing by Uta Imhoff.

Figure 6. Tongue of a *Rana* showing the deeply notched posterior end. Copied from McCranie and Wilson (2002) with permission of editor.

4 A. Skin of dorsum smooth to weakly granular, except skin can be denticulate on lower back and hind limbs; toe tips not expanded (Fig. 5); distinct dark dorsal spots usually present .... *Rana berlandieri* (**p. 47**)

  B. Skin of dorsum usually denticulate; toe tips slightly expanded (Fig. 7); dark dorsal spots, if present, usually indistinct... *Rana vaillanti* (**p. 49**)

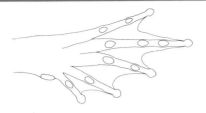

Figure 7. Ventral view of foot of *Rana vaillanti* (SMF 77975) showing extensive webbing and slightly expanded toe tips. Drawing by Uta Imhoff.

5 A. Snout protruding in lateral profile (Fig. 8); webbing between Toes I–II greatly reduced relative to webbing between other toes (Fig. 9) .... *Scinax staufferi* (**p. 39**)

  B. Snout rounded in lateral profile (Fig. 8); webbing between Toes I–II not greatly reduced relative to that between other toes.. 6

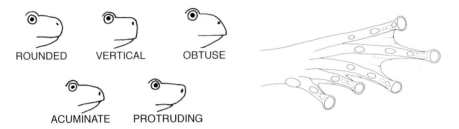

Figure 8. Snout lateral profile standards in anurans. Modified from Fig. 80 in Heyer et al. (1990) and Fig. 14 in McCranie and Wilson (2002).

Figure 9. Ventral view of foot of *Scinax staufferi* (SMF 81444) showing the webbing between Toes I–II greatly reduced relative to that between the other toes. Drawing by Uta Imhoff.

6 A. Males with paired, subgular vocal sacs (Fig. 10); size moderately large (males to 76 mm SVL, females to 90 mm SVL); dorsum usually with dark blotches
  ....*Smilisca baudinii* (**p. 41**)

  B. Males with single, median subgular vocal sac (Fig. 10); size small (females to 29 mm SVL, males to 27 mm SVL); dorsum usually with irregular dark dashes forming X-shaped mark, fragmented crossbars, fragmented lines, or reticulate pattern
  ....*Hyla microcephala* (**p. 37**)

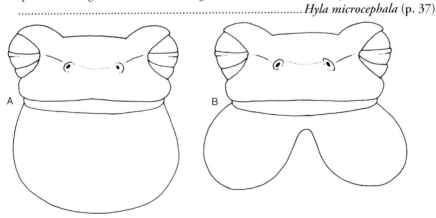

Figure 10. Male vocal sac conditions: (**A**) single, median, subgular; (**B**) paired, subgular. Copied from Duellman (2001) with permission of editor.

Family Bufonidae

The members of this family are the classic "toads," which, in Honduras, are typically squat anurans with relatively short, stocky limbs, warty skin, and prominent parotoid glands located posterior to the eyes. The head usually bears elevated cranial crests, although some species lack them. In Honduras, toads range in size from the relatively small *Atelophryniscus chrysophorus* (adult males average about 38 mm SVL and adult females about 54 mm SVL), which is endemic to the central Cordillera Nombre de Dios on the mainland, to the very large *Bufo marinus* (adult males average about 114 mm SVL and adult females about 133 mm SVL), which is extremely widespread on mainland Honduras (McCranie and Wilson, 2002). In addition to the typical "toads," this family also contains other genera and species occurring outside of Honduras that are less toadlike, such as *Atelopus*. This toad family is cosmopolitan in temperate and tropical regions, except for the Australo-Papuan (where *Bufo marinus* has been introduced), Madagascan, African Saharan, and Oceania (where *B. marinus* has also been introduced) regions. Thirty-three genera containing about 444 species were included in this family by Pough et al. (2003). Two genera comprising eight species occur in Honduras. A single species has been introduced onto the Bay Islands. None are known from the Cayos Cochinos.

Bufo marinus from the Honduran mainland. Photograph by James R. McCranie

Bufo marinus (Linnaeus, 1758)

Common name(s): Cane Toad (English; Liner, 1994); Sapo Grande (Spanish).

Description: This huge toad (Honduran males to 144 mm SVL, Honduran females to at least 177 mm, but a few reported over 200 mm in South America) has cranial crests and huge parotoid glands that extend well onto the body. Rows of enlarged dorsolateral tubercles are absent. An inner tarsal fold is present and the supernumerary tubercles are distinct. Finger webbing is absent and the toes are moderately webbed (modal webbing formula I 1—2⁺ II 1—3⁻ III 2—3 1/2 IV 3 1/2—2 V). Dorsal surfaces have numerous tubercles with dark brown to black keratinized tips. Dorsal ground color varies from pale olive green to dark brown. Adults lack a pale middorsal stripe or conspicuous interorbital bar (juveniles and subadults can have a pale middorsal stripe).

Similar species: Adults of this toad cannot be confused with any other anuran on the Bay Islands. They are huge in size and have extremely large parotoid glands behind the eyes that extend well onto the body, as well as marked cranial crests on the head. The other six species of Bay Island anurans are smaller as adults, have relatively smooth skin, and lack parotoid glands and cranial crests.

General geographic distribution: Low, moderate, and intermediate elevations from extreme southern Texas, USA, to Perú and central Brazil on the Atlantic versant and Sinaloa, Mexico, to southern Ecuador on the Pacific versant. The species also occurs naturally on the Caribbean islands of Trinidad and Tobago and is widely introduced elsewhere in the world, including, but not limited to, the Philippines, tropical Australia, Papua New Guinea, and Hawaii and southern Florida, USA.

Distribution on Las Islas de la Bahía: *Bufo marinus* is introduced on Isla de Guanaja.

Natural history comments: This toad is one of the most widely distributed anurans on mainland Honduras. It has been recorded from sea level to 1435 m elevation in lowland moist, dry, and arid forests and premontane wet, moist, and dry forests (McCranie and Wilson, 2002). Of the amphibians resident on the Islas de la Bahía,

Bufo marinus from Isla de Guanaja.
Photograph by Mikael Lundberg

only *Scinax staufferi* and *Smilisca baudinii* are about equally widely distributed on mainland Honduras, where *B. marinus* is most abundant around human habitations. The numerous fresh water swamps, marshy areas, and ponds in the vicinity of Savannah Bight offer ample areas for the reproduction of *B. marinus*.

Remarks: This toad was introduced on Isla de Guanaja. McCranie and Wilson (2002:191) reported "In February 1990, an angry resident of Isla de Guanaja told J. R. Mc-Cranie that another resident of that island had recently, and intentionally, released marine toads onto the island a few km SSW of Savannah Bight. The angry resident firmly believed that the island's snake population would become venomous if they fed on these toads. There can be little doubt that *Bufo marinus* is now firmly established on Isla de Guanaja. On 28 September 1994, G. Köhler collected a recent metamorph of *B. marinus* (SMF 77627) near North East Bight about 3 km N of Savannah Bight. Köhler returned to Isla de Guanaja in late August 1997 and found *B. marinus* adults, juveniles, and tadpoles to be abundant around Savannah Bight … ." Apparently, a local man who had sores on his legs brought several adult *B. marinus* to this island in the hope that the noxious secretions produced by the parotoid glands of this toad would help relieve his leg pain. *Bufo marinus* has already spread to a multitude of places around the world by human agency, often in an effort to control injurious insects. Introduction of *B. marinus* is apparently irreversible, as attempts at eradication in Australia have shown. What effects will occur, as a result of the introduction of this species to Guanaja, are not known. Under no circumstances, however, should this toad be transported elsewhere in the department of Islas de la Bahía. Its history of introductions elsewhere in the world should be a sufficient deterrent to halt its purposeful spread. See the Remarks for *Micrurus ruatanus* for further comments on some islanders' belief that snakes become venomous after feeding on toads.

Bufo marinus from Isla de Guanaja.
Photograph by Gunther Köhler

Family Hylidae

This is the family of typical tree frogs, although not all members are arboreal. Members usually have well developed finger and toe discs, as well as claw-shaped terminal phalanges (Pough et al., 2003). On the Bay Islands and Cayos Cochinos, these frogs are either small (*Hyla microcephala* and *Scinax staufferi*) or moderately large (*Smilisca baudinii*). The members of this family range from the southwestern portion of the Northwest Territories of Canada on the west and central Quebec, Canada, on the east to east-central Argentina. They also occur in the West Indies, the Australo-Papuan Region, and temperate Eurasia (including extreme northern Africa and the Japanese Archipelago). One species also occurs on the Azores, Madeira, and Canary Islands in the Atlantic Ocean. Forty-two genera comprising 854 species were included in this family by Duellman (2003). Ten genera containing 33 species are known to occur in Honduras. Three genera, each containing a single species, are recorded from the Bay Islands and Cayos Cochinos.

Smilisca baudinii from Isla de Roatán. Photograph by Mikael Lundberg

Hyla microcephala Cope, "1885" (1886)

Common name(s): Yellow Treefrog (English; Liner, 1994).

Description: This small frog (males to 27 mm SVL [McCranie and Wilson, 2002], females to 31 mm [Duellman, 2001]) has a well-developed axillary membrane. The snout is rounded in lateral profile. Fingers are moderately webbed (basal between Fingers I–II, remaining modal webbing formula II 1⁺—2 1/2 III 2 1/3—2⁺ IV) and the toes are extensively webbed (modal webbing formula I 1⁻—2⁻ II 3/4—2 III 3/4—2 IV 2—3/4 V). Moderately expanded disc pads with rounded disc covers are present on fingers and toes. Vomerine teeth are present. Males have a single, median, subgular vocal sac. The dorsal coloration is pale brown with a dorsal pattern usually consisting of irregular brown dashes forming an X-shaped mark, fragmented crossbars, fragmented lines, or a reticulated pattern. A thin brown dorsolateral stripe is usually present, with the brown stripe bordered above by a thin white stripe.

Similar species: Only *Scinax staufferi*, the other small hylid frog on the islands, is likely to be confused with this species. *Scinax staufferi* has a protruding snout in lateral profile, a reduced axillary membrane, and greatly reduced webbing between Toes I–II relative to that between the other toes. In addition, it has a dorsal pattern of dark brown longitudinal lines or spots on a brown background.

General geographic distribution: Low and moderate elevations on the Atlantic versant from central Veracruz and northern Oaxaca, Mexico, to southern Nicaragua and northwestern Costa Rica, additionally on the Atlantic versant from central Panamá to southeastern Brazil. It also occurs on the Pacific versant from south-central Honduras to eastern Panamá. In addition to the Bay Islands, the species also occurs on the Caribbean Islands of Trinidad and Tobago.

Hyla microcephala from the Honduran mainland. Photograph by James R. McCranie.

Hyla microcephala from Isla de Roatán.
Photograph by Mikael Lundberg

Distribution on Las Islas de la Bahía: *Hyla microcephala* occurs on Guanaja, Roatán, and Utila.

Natural history comments: *Hyla microcephala* has been collected on the Bay Islands in July, August, October, and November during the rainy season and in May during a period of light rainfall. The species forms breeding choruses around temporary ponds and inundated areas. Males call at night from grasses and other low emergent vegetation growing in and around the water. Habitat types on the Bay Islands include hardwood forest and swamps and marshes.

Hardwood forest on Isla de Roatán, May 2004. Photograph by Breck Bartholomew

Scinax staufferi (Cope, 1865)

Common name(s): Long-snout Treefrog (English*).

Description: This small frog (males to 29 mm SVL, females to 32 mm [Duellman, 2001]) has a protruding snout in lateral profile. Webbing is absent between Fingers I–II and basal between Fingers II–III–IV. Webbing between Toes I–II is greatly reduced relative to that of the other toes, which are extensively webbed (modal webbing formula I 2—2 3/4 II 1—3⁻ III 1⁺—3⁻ IV 2 1/2—1 V). Fingers and toes have large disc pads with somewhat truncated disc covers. Vomerine teeth are present. Males have a single, median, subgular vocal sac. Dorsal and lateral surfaces of the head lack distinct tubercles, although small tubercles can be present. Dorsal surfaces are some shade of brown, usually with darker brown broken longitudinal lines or stripes. The groin and anterior and posterior surfaces of the thighs are some shade of brown and the dorsal surfaces of the thighs are brown with darker brown crossbars.

Similar species: Only *Hyla microcephala*, the other small hylid on the islands, is likely to be confused with this frog. *Hyla microcephala* has a snout that is rounded in lateral profile, a well-developed axillary membrane, the webbing between Toes I–II not greatly reduced relative to that between the other toes, a thin dorsolateral dark stripe usually present and bordered above by a thin white stripe, and a dorsal pattern usually consisting of irregular dark dashes forming an **X**-shaped mark, fragmented crossbars, fragmented lines, or a reticulated pattern (occasional individual *H. microcephala* have the dorsal pattern reduced to scattered flecks).

General geographic distribution: Low, moderate, and intermediate elevations from southern Tamaulipas, Mexico, to extreme northern Costa Rica on the Atlantic versant (including Isla del Maíz Grande, Nicaragua, in addition to the Bay Islands) and from Guerrero, Mexico, to northwestern Costa Rica on the Pacific versant.

Scinax staufferi from the Honduran mainland. Photograph by James R. McCranie

Scinax staufferi from Isla de Utila.
Photograph by Gunther Köhler

Distribution on Las Islas de la Bahía: *Scinax staufferi* is recorded from Utila and Guanaja.

Natural history comments: *Scinax staufferi* has been collected on the Bay Islands in March, September, and October. It forms breeding choruses during the rainy season around inundated areas. Males call at night from grasses and other low emergent vegetation growing in and around the water. Habitat types on the Bay Islands include hardwood forest and swamps and marshes.

Remarks: *Scinax staufferi* was included in the genus *Hyla* by L. Wilson and Hahn (1973).

Scinax staufferi from the Honduran mainland. Photograph by James R. McCranie

Smilisca baudinii (Duméril and Bibron, 1841)

Common name(s): Common Treefrog (English*).

Description: This moderately large frog (males to 76 mm SVL, females to 90 mm [Duellman, 2001]) has paired subgular vocal sacs in the males. The snout is rounded in lateral profile. Fingers are moderately webbed (basal between Fingers I–II, remaining modal webbing formula II 1 2/3—2 2/3 III 2 1/3—2 IV) and the toes are extensively webbed (modal webbing formula I 1—2 II 3/4—2$^+$ III 1—2 IV 2—3/4 V). Fingers and toes have large disc pads with rounded disc covers. A row of low, distinct tubercles is usually present along the posterior ventrolateral edge of each forearm. The dorsal surfaces vary from some shade of brown to green. A brown interorbital bar and brown dorsal body blotches are usually present. A distinct dark brown to black postorbital bar or broad stripe extends above the tympanum and then downward onto the dorsolateral portion of the body to at least the level of the axilla. Contrasting dark brown vertical lip bars are present. The flanks are mottled with brown and white.

Similar species: The other hylid frogs on Las Islas de la Bahía are much smaller than this moderately large tree frog. In addition, *Scinax staufferi* has a protruding snout in lateral profile and males have a single, median subgular vocal sac. *Hyla microcephala* has a well-developed axillary membrane and the males have a single, median subgular vocal sac.

General geographic distribution: Low, moderate, and intermediate elevations from extreme southern Texas, USA, to eastern Costa Rica on the Atlantic versant and from southern Sonora, Mexico, to southeastern Costa Rica on the Pacific versant (including the Islas de Tres Marías, Nayarit, Mexico).

Smilisca baudinii from Isla de Guanaja. Photograph by Mikael Lundberg

Smilisca baudinii from the Honduran mainland.
Photograph by James R. McCranie

Distribution on Las Islas de la Bahía: *Smilisca baudinii* is distributed on Barbareta, Guanaja, Roatán, Utila, and Cayo Cochino Pequeño.

Natural history comments: Adults of *Smilisca baudinii* have been collected on the Bay Islands in February, May, July, August, October, and November and in March on the Cayos Cochinos. Tadpoles have been found on the Bay Islands in November. The species breeds during the rainy season in inundated areas, temporary ponds, and water-containing depressions in limestone rocks. Males call at night from low emergent vegetation above the breeding sites. Habitat types on the Bay Islands and Cayos Cochinos include hardwood forest and swamps and marshes.

Smilisca baudinii from the Honduran mainland. Photograph by James R. McCranie

Family Leptodactylidae

The family Leptodactylidae has no known synapomorphies (Pough et al., 2003) and, thus, may not be monophyletic. Leptodactylids are highly variable in morphology, habits, and life history (Pough et al., 2003). The member of this family on the Bay Islands and Cayos Cochinos is distinguished by the combination of having the fingers unwebbed and the toe webbing absent, basal, or only slightly developed. The members of this family occur from southeastern Arizona, southern New Mexico, south-central Texas, and extreme southern Texas, USA, to southern Chile and southern Argentina. The family also occurs throughout the West Indies. Outside of the natural range of the family, members have been widely introduced in Florida and Hawaii, USA, Bermuda, Costa Rica, and several localities in South America. Fifty-one genera containing 1106 species were included in this family by Duellman (2003). Three genera comprising 34 species are known to occur in Honduras. One species is represented on the Bay Islands and Cayos Cochinos.

Leptodactylus melanonotus from Isla de Utila. Photograph by Gunther Köhler

Leptodactylus melanonotus (Hallowell, "1860" [1861])

Common name(s): Black Ground Frog (English*).

Description: This moderately-sized frog (males to 46 mm SVL, females to 50 mm [Heyer, 1970]; Honduran specimens are smaller, however, with the largest known male being 44 mm SVL and the largest known female being 43 mm SVL [McCranie and Wilson, 2002]) lacks expanded finger and toe tips and a digital grove around the tips of the fingers and toes. The fingers are unwebbed and basal webbing is present between the toes. Well-developed lateral fleshy fringes are present on the toes. The tongue is only slightly notched posteriorly. Adult males have two thumb spines, but almost always lack hypertrophied arms. Males have paired vocal slits. The skin of the dorsal surfaces is smooth to weakly granular, usually with scattered coni apicales; occasionally small scattered tubercles can be present. Dorsolateral ridges are absent. Coni apicales are present on the ventral surfaces of the tarsal segments. Dorsal surfaces are brown to gray with indistinct darker spots present in the paler specimens. The posterior surfaces of the thighs are brown, mottled with paler brown, and the ventral surfaces are white to cream with scattered dark flecking. Brown to orange ventro-lateral glands are usually evident.

Similar species: No other species of anuran on Las Islas de la Bahía is likely to be confused with this one, except, perhaps, for small specimens of *Rana*. Both *Rana berlandieri* and *R. vaillanti*, however, have toes with extensive webbing, dorsolateral ridges, and a tongue that is deeply notched posteriorly. In addition, *Rana berlandieri* usually has a spotted or blotched dorsum.

General geographic distribution: Low, moderate, and intermediate elevations from Tamaulipas, Mexico, to central Panamá on the Atlantic versant and from Sonora, Mexico, to Ecuador on the Pacific versant.

Leptodactylus melanonotus from Isla de Roatán. Photograph by James R. McCranie

Leptodactylus melanonotus from Isla de Guanaja. Photograph by Mikael Lundberg

Distribution on Las Islas de la Bahía: *Leptodactylus melanonotus* is known from Barbareta, Guanaja, Roatán, Utila, and Cayo Cochino Grande.

Natural history comments: Adults of *Leptodactylus melanonotus* have been collected during the rainy season in July, August, October, and November on the Bay Islands and during the dry season in March on the Cayos Cochinos. Males call at night from concealed places on the ground around inundated areas and along small, slow-moving streams. In addition to calling at night, males also frequently call throughout the day at the height of the breeding season. Tadpoles of this species were in temporary ponds on the Bay Islands in November, January, and February. Habitat types on the Bay Islands and Cayos Cochinos include hardwood forest, pine forest, and swamps and marshes.

Leptodactylus melanonotus from the Honduran mainland. Photograph by James R. McCranie

Family Ranidae

This family lacks any known synapomorphies (Pough et al., 2003) and may be polyphyletic. Members of this family on the Islas de la Bahía are distinguished by the combination of having the fingers unwebbed, the toes extensively webbed, the tongue deeply notched posteriorly, and parotoid glands absent. It ranges in the Western Hemisphere from northern Alaska, USA, on the west and northern Quebec, Canada, on the east to north-central Bolivia and eastern Brazil. Outside of the Western Hemisphere, this family is generally missing only from Saharan Africa, much of Australia, New Zealand, and high latitude regions. Fifty-one genera comprising 686 species were included in this family by Duellman (2003), but the taxonomy of this family "is still very problematic" (Dubois, 1999:81). One genus containing five species occurs in Honduras. Two species are recorded from the Islas de la Bahía.

Rana berlandieri from Isla de Roatán.
Photograph by Breck Bartholomew

Rana berlandieri Baird, 1859

Common name(s): Spotted Pond Frog (English*).

Description: This large frog (males to 88 mm SVL, females to 117 mm [McCranie and Wilson, 2002]) lacks expanded toe tips and a digital groove around the tips of the toes. Fingers are unwebbed and toes are extensively webbed (modal webbing formula I 1/4—2 II 1/4—2 1/3 III 1—2$^+$ IV 2 1/2—1/4 V). Lateral keels or fleshy fringes are present on the unwebbed portions of the toes. An outer metatarsal tubercle is absent. The tongue is deeply notched posteriorly. Adult males have a well-developed gray thumb pad. Adult males usually have small, poorly developed, paired vocal slits and paired, lateral vocal sacs located posterior to the angle of the jaw. The skin of the dorsal surfaces is smooth to weakly granular, except that the skin is occasionally denticulate on the lower back and on the hind limbs. Distinct dorsolateral ridges are present. Dorsal surfaces are pale green to brown, almost always with distinct dark brown spots or blotches on the back. The posterior surfaces of the thighs are mottled dark and pale brown, or have small pale brown spots on a darker brown ground color. The ventral surfaces are pale yellow to white; small brown spots or flecking are occasionally present on the chin, throat, and chest.

Similar species: *Leptodactylus melanonotus* is a smaller frog with only basal toe webbing and a tongue that is only slightly notched posteriorly. *Rana vaillanti* has denticulate skin on the dorsum, slightly expanded toe tips, and the dorsum of the body lacking distinct dark dorsal spots (dark dorsal spots, if present, usually indistinct).

General geographic distribution: Low, moderate, and intermediate elevations of the Atlantic versant from extreme southeastern New Mexico and central Texas, USA, to northern Nicaragua. Also found on the Pacific versant in Oaxaca and eastern Guerrero, Mexico (see Remarks).

Rana berlandieri from the Honduran mainland. Photograph by James R. McCranie

Rana berlandieri from Isla de Utila.
Photograph by Gunther Köhler

Distribution on Las Islas de la Bahía: *Rana berlandieri* is recorded from Roatán and Utila.

Natural history comments: Adults of *Rana berlandieri* have been collected on the Bay Islands during February, May, June, October, and November around temporary ponds, slow-moving streams, and marshy areas. Males call at night while sitting in or floating on the surface of these water bodies. Tadpoles from the Bay Islands were collected during February and November from slow-moving streams. Habitat types on the Bay Islands include hardwood forest and swamps and marshes.

Remarks: The range given in the General geographic distribution section probably encompasses ranges of more than one species, and the Honduran populations are not likely to be conspecific with those from the vicinity of the type locality (McCranie and Wilson, 2002). L. Wilson and Hahn (1973) included this species under the name *Rana pipiens* in their report on the herpetofauna of the Bay Islands.

Rana vaillanti Brocchi, 1877

Common name(s): Guanaja Pond Frog (English*).

Description: This large frog (males to 94 mm SVL, females to 125 mm [Hillis and de Sá, 1988]) has slightly expanded toe tips without marginal grooves laterally. Fingers are unwebbed and toes are extensively webbed (modal webbing formula I 1/4—1 1/3 II 1/4—2⁻ III 1/4—2⁻ IV 1 1/2—1/4 V). Lateral fleshy fringes are present on the unwebbed portions of the toes. An outer metatarsal tubercle is absent. The tympanum is large (tympanum length/eye length >0.700). The tongue is deeply notched posteriorly. Adult males have a well-developed thumb pad that is usually not darker than the rest of the thumb. Adult males usually have small, poorly developed, paired vocal slits and internal, paired vocal sacs are usually present. The skin of the dorsal surfaces is denticulate. Distinct dorsolateral ridges are present. Dorsal surfaces are some shade of brown, usually with a greenish color anteriorly. A dark eye mask is occasionally present. A pale supralabial stripe is usually absent; when present, a pale stripe is usually located only posterior to the eye. The posterior surfaces of the thighs are mottled dark and pale brown. The ventral surfaces are white with a bronze sheen (cream to white in preservative), usually lightly flecked with gray or brown, occasionally densely flecked or mottled with dark brown.

Similar species: *Leptodactylus melanonotus* is a smaller frog with only basal toe webbing and a tongue that is only slightly notched posteriorly. *Rana berlandieri* has the skin of the dorsum smooth to weakly granular, unexpanded toe tips, and distinct dark dorsal spots usually present.

General geographic distribution: Low and moderate elevations from north-central Veracruz and northern Oaxaca, Mexico, to the central Río Magdalena region in Colombia on the Atlantic versant and on the Pacific versant in southeastern Oaxaca and northwestern

Rana vaillanti from the Honduran mainland. Photograph by James R. McCranie

Rana vaillanti from Isla de Guanaja.
Photograph by Gunther Köhler

Chiapas, Mexico, from northwestern Nicaragua to northwestern Costa Rica, and from western Panamá to southern Ecuador.

Distribution on Las Islas de la Bahía: *Rana vaillanti* is recorded only from Guanaja.

Natural history comments: *Rana vaillanti* has been collected on Guanaja during February and August and from sometime between December and March (see McCranie and Wilson, 2002). It is known for certain only from swampy areas near Savannah Bight, where it has been seen at night sitting along edges of the water.

Remarks: The populations of this frog from Guanaja were described as a distinct species, *Rana bonaccana*, by Günther in 1901. Hillis and de Sá (1988) synonymized *R. bonaccana* with *R. vaillanti*. L. Wilson and Hahn (1973) included this species under the name *R. palmipes*.

Class Reptilia (Reptiles)

The members of the class Reptilia (following the classification of Pough et al., 2003), called reptiles, are tetrapod vertebrates, as are amphibians, but, unlike amphibians, reptiles are amniote vertebrates, i.e., they possess a type of egg termed the amniotic or cleidoic egg, which is adapted for laying on land, and, in fact, cannot be laid in water (thus, aquatic reptiles must come out on land to lay their eggs). Reptiles were the first vertebrate animals to make a complete transition from aquatic environments to terrestrial ones. Reptiles do not have larval stages in their life cycles; what hatches from the egg, or is born, is a miniature of the adult (i.e., they have direct development). Although most reptiles lay eggs, giving birth to living young (viviparity) has evolved in many reptilian lineages, and, in fact, some of the snakes found on the Bay Islands and Cayos Cochinos give birth to living young (e.g., *Boa constrictor*).

Five orders of living reptiles are extant (Pough et al., 2003). These orders are the Testudines or Chelonia, Rhynchocephalia, Squamata, Crocodylia, and Aves. Four of these five orders are traditionally considered within the provenance of herpetology. The fifth group, the Aves or birds, are traditionally handled within the discipline of ornithology. Nonetheless, modern classificatory (i.e., cladistic) procedure places the birds as an order within the class Reptilia. They, however, are not dealt with herein beyond this point. The members of the Testudines are the turtles, which are a group of shelled, quadruped, largely cosmopolitan reptiles. The two living members of the order Rhynchocephalia are the tuataras, which are lizardlike reptiles restricted in distribution to New Zealand. The members of the order Squamata are the amphisbaenians, lizards, and snakes, which are a group of largely cosmopolitan reptiles with highly kinetic skulls and paired copulatory organs called hemipenes. The members of the order Crocodylia are the crocodilians, a group of largely pantropical, heavily armored reptiles with long snouts, elongate bodies, and powerful limbs and tails (Pough et al., 2003). Turtles, crocodilians, lizards, and snakes are all represented in the herpetofauna of the Bay Islands and Cayos Cochinos.

Key to the Orders of Reptiles

1 A. Body encased in a shell, which encloses girdles; no teeth present, jaws enclosed in a horny sheath ....**Testudines (p. 54)**
   B. Body not encased in a shell; teeth present on jaws 2
2 A. Cloacal opening longitudinal; teeth in sockets ....**Crocodylia (p. 52)**
   B. Cloacal opening transverse; teeth not in sockets ....**Squamata (p. 66)**

Order Crocodylia (Crocodilians)

Crocodilians are large, lizardlike reptiles in general appearance (Fig. 11). "Crocodilians have heavily armored, elongate bodies with long snouts and powerful tails and limbs. The armor is formed by heavy plates of bone (osteoderms) that lie within the dermis, underneath the heavy epidermal scales. Osteoderms are also present ventrally in many species" (Pough et al., 2003:166–167). Only one (*Crocodylus acutus*) of the two crocodilian species recorded from Honduras (L. Wilson and McCranie, 2002) lives on the Islas de la Bahía. It inhabits brackish water estuaries in mangrove forests.

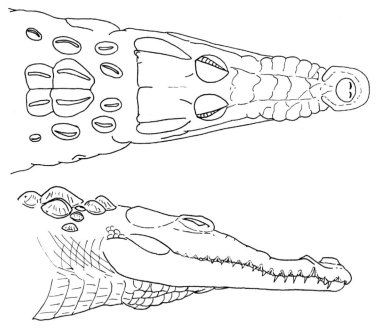

Figure 11. Head and forebody of *Crocodylus acutus* (SMF 26339). Drawing by Milan Vesely.

Family Crocodylidae

"In crocodylids, the fourth tooth in the lower jaw is accommodated in a notch in the upper jaw and is visible when the mouth is closed" (Pough et al., 2003:171). The members of this family of crocodilians, in the Western Hemisphere, range in coastal southern Florida and the Florida Keys, USA, coastal Cuba (and adjacent islands), Hispaniola, Jamaica, and the Cayman Islands, both coasts of Mexico from northern Sinaloa and central Tamaulipas southward through Central America to northern South America from Colombia to the mouth of the Orinoco River in Venezuela on the Atlantic side and Colombia to extreme northwestern Perú on the Pacific side. In the Eastern Hemisphere, they are distributed in tropical Africa, India, southern China, Indochina, and northern Australia. Two genera containing 13 species presently are included in this family (Pough et al., 2003). Only one species occurs in Honduras, and it is also found on the Bay Islands.

Crocodylus acutus Cuvier, 1807

Common name(s): Alligator (English); Cocodrilo, Lagarto (Spanish).

Description: *Crocodylus acutus* is a large crocodile that can reach lengths in excess of 6 m (adults usually 3 to 4 m TL) and weigh over 1,000 kg. Hatchling length is 20 to 35 cm TL (Ernst et al., 1999). The snout is long and pointed, with the fourth tooth of the lower jaw clearly visible when the mouth is closed. A preorbital transverse ridge is absent. Two to 4 postoccipital scutes are arranged in a single transverse row and 0 to 6 nuchal scutes (usually 4 in 2 juxtaposed pairs) are present. Fourteen to 18 transverse rows of dorsal scutes occur in 2 to 6 (usually 4) longitudinal rows at midbody and 25 to 35 transverse rows of ventral scales are present. The dental formula is 5+13–14/15. Adults are gray, brownish gray, or olive dorsally, with dark markings or banding on the body and tail. The ventral surfaces are cream or white.

Similar species: No other reptiles on the Bay Islands can be confused with this crocodile.

General geographic distribution: Low and moderate elevations from Sinaloa, Mexico, to extreme northwestern Perú on the Pacific versant and from Tabasco, Mexico, to northeastern Venezuela on the Atlantic versant. The species is also known from southern Florida, USA, and the islands of Cuba, Little Cayman, Cayman Brac, Jamaica, Hispaniola, Martinique, and Margarita. It also has been reported from Isla de Coiba, Panamá.

Distribution on Las Islas de la Bahía: *Crocodylus acutus* is known to occur on Barbareta, Roatán, and Utila. Residents of the eastern end of Roatán told McCranie in 1989 that crocodiles still occurred on Morat (an island between Roatán and Barbareta).

Natural history comments: Kaiser et al. (2001b) reported a breeding population of *Crocodylus acutus* on the eastern end of Isla de Roatán. McCranie saw and photographed a skin of an individual of this species taken from an adult that was killed in 1989 in a gully near Sandy Bay on Roatán. McCranie also saw an adult (ca. 3 m) swimming at dusk in a brackish pond on the south shore of Barbareta in February 1990. *Crocodylus acutus* is a semi-aquatic species that occurs in mangrove forest and estuaries or brackish water ponds on the Bay Islands. The female constructs and lays her eggs in a nest of debris above the high tide line. She remains in association with the nest until the eggs hatch and with the young for a period of time thereafter. The species' populations on the Bay Islands have been severely depleted.

Crocodylus acutus from the Honduran mainland. Photograph by Gunther Köhler

Order Testudines (Turtles)

Turtles are reptiles that possess a shell composed of a dorsal portion (the carapace; Fig. 12) and a ventral portion (the plastron; Fig. 13). "The shell is composed of dermal ossifications incorporating the ribs, vertebrae [except for those of the neck and tail], and portions of the pectoral girdle" (Pough et al., 2003:97). The ribs are fused to the lateral portion of the carapace and enclose the pectoral and pelvic girdles, a unique arrangement among vertebrate animals (Pough et al., 2003). The bony portions of the shell are overlain usually by keratinous scutes. In a few cases, as in the leatherback sea turtle, for example, the dermal bony elements are covered with a leathery skin (Pough et al., 2003). Three of the five species of turtles known from the Islas de la Bahía are sea turtles, which have the limbs modified into paddles. Of the non-marine species, one is an emydid turtle, *Trachemys venusta*, and the other is a kinosternid turtle, *Kinosternon leucostomum*. All turtles are oviparous, thus those occurring on the Islas de la Bahía must lay their eggs on land, as the eggs cannot withstand immersion in water. The eggs are laid in excavations dug by the female.

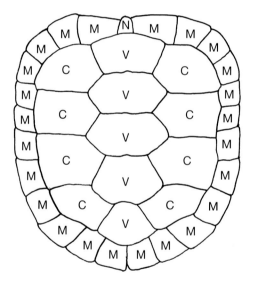
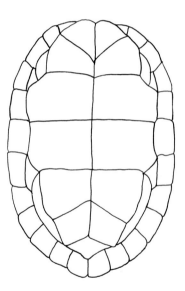

Figure 12. Carapace of a turtle (*Trachemys venusta*; SMF 77494) showing the scutes mentioned in various species accounts. C = costal scute; M = marginal scute; N = nuchal scute; and V = vertebral scute. Drawing by Philipp Groß.

Figure 13. Plastron of a turtle (*Trachemys venusta*; SMF 77494) showing 12 plastral scutes and unhinged plastron. Drawing by Philipp Groß.

Key to the Species of Turtles of the Bay Islands and Cayos Cochinos

1   **A.** Forelimbs paddlelike; marine.. 2
    B. Forelimbs not paddlelike; non-marine 4
2   **A.** Five or more pairs of costal scutes present; nuchal scute contacts first pair of costal scutes ....*Caretta caretta* (**p. 56**)
    B. Four pairs of costal scutes present; nuchal scute not in contact with first pair of costal scutes 3
3   **A.** Two pairs of prefrontal scales (Fig. 14); carapacial scutes imbricate; upper jaw hooked (Fig. 14)..*Eretmochelys imbricata* (**p. 60**)
    B. A single pair of prefrontal scales (Fig. 15); carapacial scutes non-overlapping; upper jaw not hooked (Fig. 15) ....*Chelonia mydas* (**p. 58**)

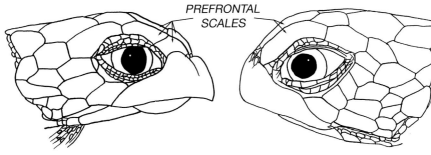

PREFRONTAL SCALES

Figure 14. Head of *Eretmochelys imbricata* showing two pairs of prefrontal scales and a hooked upper jaw. Drawing by Philipp Groß.

Figure 15. Head of *Chelonia mydas* showing a single pair of prefrontal scales and an unhooked upper jaw. Drawing by Philipp Groß.

4   **A.** Twelve plastral scutes present (Fig. 13); plastron unhinged
    .... *Trachemys venusta* (**p. 62**)
    B. Eleven plastral scutes present (Fig. 16); plastron with anterior and posterior hinges (Fig. 16) ....*Kinosternon leucostomum* (**p. 64**)

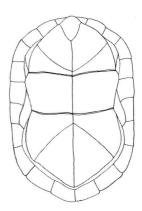

Figure 16. Plastron of *Kinosternon leucostomum* (SMF 79845) showing 11 plastral scutes and anterior and posterior hinges. Drawing by Philipp Groß.

Family Cheloniidae

The limbs are modified into fully webbed paddles and the members of this family are wholly marine, except that the females come ashore to lay eggs (Pough et al., 2003), and at least one species is known to bask on shore. This family of turtles ranges circumglobally in temperate and tropical oceans. Six species in five genera are currently included in this family (Pough et al., 2003). The paddlelike limbs of this family are unique among the turtles known to occur on the Islas de la Bahía. Four species in separate genera are currently known to occupy Honduran waters, and three of those have been recorded from the Bay Islands.

Caretta caretta (Linnaeus, 1758)

Common name(s): Loggerhead (English); Tortuga Caguama (Spanish).

Description: This very large sea turtle can reach a carapace length of 700 to 1000 mm and weigh 70 to160 kg (Savage, 2002). The shield-shaped carapace is widest towards the anterior end, has serrate margins, and non-overlapping scutes (except scutes imbricate in some young specimens). The first of 5 pairs of costal scutes is in contact with the nuchal scute. The juvenile carapace is tricarinate, with the median keel knobbed, although these keels are lost in adults. The plastron is unhinged, and hatchlings often have 2 longitudinal plastral ridges. Twelve plastral scutes are arranged in 6 pairs and a small intergular scute often is present. Two pairs of prefrontal scales are present that sometimes form a median suture, but most often an additional azygous scale or scales are present. The large, robust head has a smooth-margined lower jaw. Limbs are developed into paddlelike flippers, each with 2 small claws. The tail of males extends beyond the carapacial margin, whereas the tail of females barely reaches the carapacial margin. The carapace is reddish-brown, often with

Caretta caretta from an unknown locality. Photographed at the Miami Seaquarium in July 1974 by James R. McCranie

Caretta caretta hatchling from the Bahamas. Photograph © James D. Watt/SeaPics.com

algae or barnacles attached and the plastron ranges from yellowish white to yellowish brown. The head can be various shades of brown, with some lateral scales exhibiting some shade of red centrally and yellow on the margins. The limbs and tail are brown dorsally and yellow ventrally.

Similar species: Only the two other sea turtles (*Chelonia mydas* and *Eretmochelys imbricata*) have the appendages modified as paddles or flippers. *Chelonia mydas* and *Eretmochelys imbricata* have four pairs of costal scutes, with the first pair separated from the nuchal scute.

General geographic distribution: This species has a nearly cosmopolitan distribution, "…inhabiting continental shelves, bays, estuaries, and lagoons in the temperate, subtropical, and tropical waters of the Atlantic, Pacific, and Indian oceans. Major nesting grounds are generally located in warm temperate and subtropical regions" (Dodd, 1990:483.2).

Distribution on Las Islas de la Bahía: *Caretta caretta* has been recorded only from Guanaja and Utila.

Natural history comments: *Caretta caretta* is strictly a marine turtle, with only the females coming ashore, and then only to lay eggs. The species is known to occasionally nest during May and June on Pumpkin Hill Beach, Utila (Köhler, pers. observ.).

Remarks: People on the Bay Islands exploit eggs of *Caretta caretta* as a food source. Also, the meat of this species is highly prized in many parts of its range. As a result, populations of this turtle are severely depleted throughout the world.

Chelonia mydas (Linnaeus, 1758)

Common name(s): Green Sea Turtle (English); Tortuga Verde (Spanish).

Description: This large sea turtle typically reaches a carapace length between 900 and 1220 mm, but has been reported to reach 1530 mm and weigh 295 kg or more (Savage, 2002). The somewhat rounded, heart shaped carapace is broad and low with smooth margins and the dorsal scutes are juxtaposed. The first of 4 pairs of costal scutes is separated from the nuchal scute. Hatchlings usually have a middorsal keel on the carapace, whereas adults lack dorsal keels or ridges. The plastron is unhinged, and hatchlings often have 2 longitudinal plastral keels. Six pairs of plastral scutes and a large intergular scute are present. One pair of prefrontal scales is present. The lower jaw (mandible) is strongly serrated. Limbs are developed into paddlelike flippers, each with usually a single small claw. The tail of males has a flattened, keratinized tip and extends well beyond the margin of the carapace, whereas the tail of females lacks a keratinized tip and does not extend beyond the margin of the carapace. The carapace is usually brown, often with infusions of darker mottling, wavy lines, or blotches and the plastron is cream or pale yellow. The scales on the dorsal surfaces of the head, limbs, and tail are dark brown or grayish black with pale margins. Ventral surfaces are cream or pale yellow.

Similar species: Only the two other sea turtles (*Caretta caretta* and *Eretmochelys imbricata*) have the appendages modified as paddles or flippers. *Caretta caretta* has five or more pairs of costal scutes, the first pair of which is in contact with the nuchal scute. *Eretmochelys imbricata* has two pairs of prefrontal scales and the mandible only weakly serrated.

General geographic distribution: This species occurs in tropical and subtropical seas, normally between the 20°C isotherms.

Distribution on Las Islas de la Bahía: *Chelonia mydas* has only been recorded from Roatán and Utila.

Chelonia mydas from Isla de Roatán.
Photograph © Doug Perrine/SeaPics.com

Chelonia mydas hatchling from Dominica.
Photograph by © Rowan Byrne/SeaPics.com

Natural history comments: Although a marine turtle, *Chelonia mydas* is known to bask on the shore. McCranie saw a hatchling of this species in captivity on the eastern portion of Roatán in November 1989, suggesting that perhaps this species occasionally nests on the Islas de la Bahía.

Remarks: The common name of this turtle is derived from the greenish color of its body fat (Ernst and Barbour, 1989). The meat and eggs of *Chelonia mydas* are a highly prized source of protein for people in the region. Thus, its Caribbean populations are severely depleted.

Chelonia mydas from the Cayman Islands.
Photograph © Doug Perrine/SeaPics.com

Eretmochelys imbricata (Linnaeus, 1766)

Common name(s): Hawksbill (English); Tortuga Carey (Spanish).

Description: This medium-sized sea turtle typically reaches a carapace length from 750 to 900 mm, but can reach 1140 mm and weigh up to 127 kg (Savage, 2002). The carapace is relatively long and narrow in adults, but more heart-shaped in juveniles. The margins are strongly serrated posteriorly, and in most individuals the dorsal scutes are imbricate (juveniles and very old animals have dorsal scutes that do not overlap). The first of 4 pairs of costal scutes is not in contact with the nuchal scute. Hatchlings usually have a middorsal keel on the carapace. The plastron is unhinged, and hatchlings often have 2 longitudinal plastral ridges. Six pairs of plastral scutes and a large intergular scute are present. The relatively narrow head has 2 pairs of prefrontal scales, a somewhat hooked upper jaw, and a lower jaw (mandible) with a smooth margin. Limbs are paddlelike, each usually with 2 small claws. Males have long tails that extend well beyond the margin of the carapace, whereas the tail of females extends to the edge of or just slightly beyond the margin of the carapace. The carapacial scutes are brown with a distinct black, tan, and cream pattern, and can have a glossy sheen. The plastron is yellow or yellow-orange. Dorsal scales on the head and appendages are generally brown or reddish-brown, with pale margins. Ventral surfaces of the head and appendages are pale yellow.

Similar species: Only the two other sea turtles (*Caretta caretta* and *Chelonia mydas*) have the appendages modified as paddles or flippers. *Caretta caretta* has five or more pairs of costal scutes, the first pair of which is in contact with the nuchal scute. *Chelonia mydas* has a single pair of prefrontal scales and a strongly serrated mandible.

General geographic distribution: This species occurs worldwide in tropical and subtropical seas, and occasionally ranges into some temperate seas.

Eretmochelys imbricata from an unknown locality. Photographed at the Miami Seaquarium in July 1974 by James R. McCranie

Eretmochelys imbricata from an unknown locality. Photographed in captivity on Isla de Roatán by Breck Bartholomew

Distribution on Las Islas de la Bahía: *Eretmochelys imbricata* has been recorded from Guanaja, Utila, and Cayo Cochino Pequeño. Also, shells of this species can be seen in bars and several tourist shops on Roatán.

Natural history comments: *Eretmochelys imbricata* is strictly a marine turtle, with only the females coming ashore, and then only to deposit eggs. This species is known to occasionally nest during May and June at Pumpkin Hill Beach, Utila (Köhler, pers. observ.).

Remarks: People in the region use eggs of *Eretmochelys imbricata* as a source of protein. The shells of this species have also been highly exploited for thousands of years worldwide, thus populations are severely depleted worldwide.

Eretmochelys imbricata hatchling from Dominica. Photograph © Rowan Byrne/ SeaPics.com

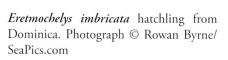

Family Emydidae

Emydid turtles are primarily aquatic to semiaquatic, occurring in both fresh and brackish water environments, although a few members are terrestrial (Pough et al., 2003). This family of turtles ranges in the Western Hemisphere from southern Canada, through much of the USA, much of Mexico, and Central America, with disjunct distribution in South America as far south as southern Brazil, Uruguay, and northeastern Argentina; it is also distributed in the Bahamas and the Greater Antilles. In the Eastern Hemisphere, the family occurs in Europe, western Asia, and northern Africa. Twelve genera comprising 40 species were included in this family by Pough et al. (2003), but the family's content remains controversial. Only one species is known to occur in Honduras, including the Islas de la Bahía.

Trachemys venusta (Gray, 1855)

Common name(s): Slider (English*); Jícotea (Spanish).

Description: This moderately-sized turtle exhibits strong sexual size dimorphism, with adult females reaching 600 mm in carapace length, and males reaching a maximum of 340 mm (Savage, 2002). The carapace has a well-defined median keel in juveniles, the keel becoming reduced to absent in older individuals. The posterior margin of the carapace is serrate. The ovate plastron is unhinged and posteriorly notched, and the plastron of adult males bears no pronounced concavity. Twelve plastral scutes are arranged in 6 pairs. The upper jaw is notched and the alveolar surface is broad and ridged. Feet are extensively webbed. The carapace is green to gray, with ocellate yellow-orange lines with dark borders and centers on the costal and vertebral scutes. The plastron is yellow with a dark brown lined symmetrical figure, and with dark ocelli on the underside of the marginal scutes. The head is green to gray, with a well-defined yellow supratemporal stripe that contacts the orbit. A broad yellow

Trachemys venusta from the Honduran mainland.
Photograph by Gunther Köhler

Trachemys venusta from the Honduran mainland. Photograph by James R. McCranie

or reddish orange supratympanic stripe is also present and in contact with the orbit. Numerous narrow yellow (with black borders) stripes are also present on all surfaces of the head (all head stripes can become obscure or absent in old individuals). Soft parts are generally greenish gray with streaks of yellow and black and the tail has paired yellow stripes above and below, with the dorsal stripes fusing distally.

Similar species: No other turtle on Las Islas de la Bahía is likely to be confused with this one. The sea turtles all have paddlelike front limbs and live in marine waters. *Kinosternon leucostomum* has 11 plastral scutes and a double-hinged plastron.

General geographic distribution: Low and moderate elevations of the Atlantic versant from northern Tamaulipas, Mexico, to extreme northern Colombia; also on the Pacific versant from southern Oaxaca, Mexico, to southwestern Guatemala, El Salvador, and from west-central Costa Rica to northwestern Colombia. The species also occurs on several islands off the coast of mainland Central America.

Distribution on Las Islas de la Bahía: *Trachemys venusta* is known from Roatán, Utila, and Cayo Cochino Grande.

Natural history comments: *Trachemys venusta* is an aquatic turtle that occurs in estuaries and brackish water marshes on the Bay Islands and Cayos Cochinos. McCranie saw a captive adult of this species in Coxen Hole, Roatán during November 1989. The owner said he had captured the turtle in a brackish water marsh near that town, and that he planned on eating the turtle's meat.

Remarks: *Trachemys venusta* was included under the names *Chrysemys ornata* by L. Wilson and Hahn (1973) and *Trachemys scripta* by L. Wilson and Cruz Díaz (1993). Seidel (2002) partitioned the polytypic species *Trachemys scripta* into 15 allopatric species (one of which is *T. venusta*), and this species group will likely undergo further revision upon future study.

Family Kinosternidae

Kinosternid turtles are generally small (110 to 200 mm in carapace length), although some tropical species can reach nearly 400 mm. They possess cloacal glands that release a foul-smelling musk. They tend to walk along the bottoms of slow-moving streams and ponds and are poor swimmers. The distribution of the members of this family is limited to the Western Hemisphere. It occurs from the eastern, central and southwestern USA, through Mexico and Central America to South America as far south as northern Argentina. Three genera comprising 22 species were included in this family by Pough et al. (2003). Two genera containing three species are currently known to range into Honduras. Only one species is found on the Islas de la Bahía.

Kinosternon leucostomum (Duméril and Bibron, *in* Duméril and Duméril, 1851)

Common name(s): Mud Turtle (English*).

Description: This small turtle can exceed 175 mm in carapace length in adult males, with females being slightly smaller (Berry and Iverson, 2001). The ovoid carapace is unicarinate (keel can be absent or indistinct in some old individuals) and the marginals anterior and posterior to the bridge are moderately to distinctly flared. The plastron has two hinges, the anterior hinge being the more kinetic of the two, with these hinges allowing for complete closure of the shell in the Cayos Cochinos populations. Eleven plastral scutes are arranged in 5 pairs. A single intergular scute is broader on the dorsal surface of the plastron than on the ventral surface. In males, the plastron is usually slightly smaller and more concave than that of the female. Upper jaw is hooked and both the upper and the lower jaw margins are smooth. One or more pairs of small barbels are present in the gular region.

Kinosternon leucostomum from the Honduran mainland. Photograph by James R. McCranie

Kinosternon leucostomum from the Honduran mainland. Photograph by Mikael Lundberg

The feet are webbed, and adult males have patches of spiny scales on the calf and thigh of the hind limbs that are used to clasp females during mating. The tail is short, but longer in males than in females. Both sexes have a terminal spine on the tail, which is larger in males. Carapace is brown to black and the plastron is yellow to pale brown, with some seams dark brown. The head is dark brown to gray dorsally and laterally with cream to pale brown spots and/or reticulations present laterally and usually dorsally. A cream, yellow, or pale brown postorbital stripe extending from the upper posterior portion of the eye onto the lateral area of the neck can be present (distinct or obscure) or absent altogether. The jaw sheaths are cream to yellow, with dark vertical lines present in some older males. The limbs and soft parts are brown or gray dorsally and yellowish to pale brown ventrally.

Similar species: No other turtle on Las Islas de la Bahía is likely to be confused with this one. The sea turtles all have paddlelike front limbs and live in marine waters. *Trachemys venusta* has 12 plastral scutes and an unhinged plastron.

General geographic distribution: Low and moderate elevations from central Veracruz, Mexico, to north-central Colombia on the Atlantic versant and from west-central Costa Rica to extreme northwestern Perú on the Pacific versant. It also occurs on Isla del Maíz Grande, Nicaragua, in addition to Cayo Cochino Grande.

Distribution on Las Islas de la Bahía: *Kinosternon leucostomum* is known only from Cayo Cochino Grande.

Natural history comments: L. Wilson and Cruz Díaz (1993:15) recorded a single specimen of this species from Cayo Cochino Grande that was "sitting at night on a plank across one of the fingers of the estuary at La Ensenada."

Order Squamata (Lizards and Snakes)

Squamate reptiles are commonly referred to as lizards, snakes, and amphisbaenians (the last do not occur in Honduras). Typically, squamates have a highly kinetic skull, compared to that of turtles, crocodilians, and the New Zealand tuatara. In addition, they possess a pair of male copulatory organs called hemipenes, which are outpocketings of the posterior wall of the cloaca residing in the base of the tail of the male (Pough et al., 2003). Amphisbaenians and snakes are groups nested within the Scleroglossa, a group of squamates also including several lizard families (Pough et al., 2003). Thus, the traditional separation of squamate reptiles into two suborders is not substantiated on modern evolutionary grounds. Nonetheless, in the region covered by this book, snakes can easily be distinguished from lizards, inasmuch as the lizards all have four well-developed limbs and the snakes do not (although *Boa constrictor* does have cloacal spurs, which are external remnants of posterior limbs). Lizards and snakes are dealt with in separate sections below.

Lizards

Eighty-eight species of lizards have been recorded for Honduras (L. Wilson and McCranie, 2002), of which 23 occur on the Bay Islands and Cayos Cochinos (Tables 1 and 2). These species are easily distinguishable from the 19 snake species, since they have four well-developed limbs, as noted above, and an external ear opening. In addition, most species, save for those within the genera *Gymnophthalmus, Hemidactylus, Phyllodactylus,*

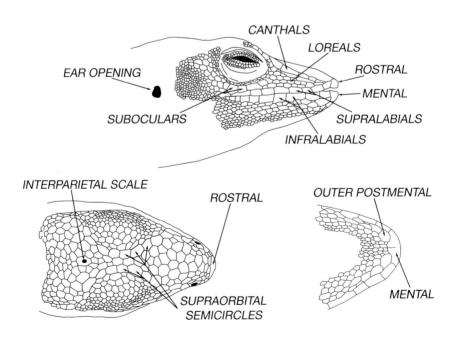

Figure 17. Drawings of a lizard head showing pertinent scale characters. Drawings by Gunther Köhler.

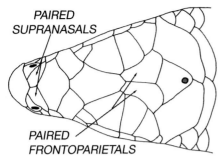

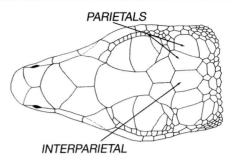

Figure 18. Dorsal view of head of *Mabuya unimarginata* (SMF 79851) showing paired supranasal (internasal) and frontoparietal scales. Drawing by Uta Imhoff.

Figure 19. Dorsal view of head of *Cnemidophorus lemniscatus* (SMF 77111) showing parietal and interparietal scales. Drawing by Uta Imhoff.

Sphaerodactylus, and *Thecadactylus*, have moveable eyelids. In Honduras, they range in size from the diminutive *Sphaerodactylus* to the large *Ctenosaura* and *Iguana*. Some of the lizard head scales mentioned in the various species descriptions are shown in Figs. 17–19.

Key to the Species of Lizards of the Bay Islands and Cayos Cochinos

1 **A.** No moveable eyelids 2
   B. Moveable eyelids present 7
2 **A.** Dorsal surface of head covered with enlarged, platelike scales (Fig. 20)
       .... *Gymnophthalmus speciosus* (p. 118)
   B. Dorsal surface of head covered with granular scales................................. 3

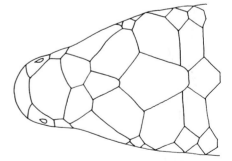

Figure 20. Dorsal view of head of *Gymnophthalmus speciosus* (SMF 78136) showing large platelike scales. Drawing by Uta Imhoff.

3 **A.** Several lamellae (or at least terminal lamellae) beneath toes expanded and double (Fig. 21) 4
   B. Lamellae beneath toes not expanded or, if expanded, they are single (Fig. 21)........ 6
4 **A.** More than 12 divided subdigital lamellae on Digit IV of hands and feet, the distalmost widely separated by skin (Fig. 21) .... *Thecadactylus rapicauda* (p. 84)
   B. Fewer than 12 subdigital lamellae on Digit IV of hands and feet, none widely separated by skin 5

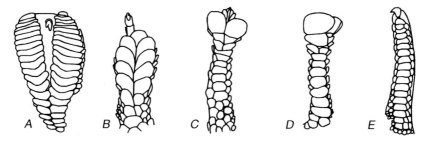

Figure 21. Subdigital lamellae: (a) *Thecadactylus rapicauda* (SMF 78555); (b) *Hemidactylus frenatus* (SMF 77544); (c) *Phyllodactylus tuberculosus* (SMF 43143); (d) *Sphaerodactylus millepunctatus* (SMF 77998); and (e) *Coleonyx mitratus* (SMF 77980). Modified from Fig. 105 in Köhler (2003).

5   **A.** Distal pair of subdigital lamellae expanded to form leaflike pads (Fig. 21)
.... *Phyllodactylus palmeus* (p. 78)
    B. Distal pair of subdigital lamellae not expanded to form leaflike pads (Fig. 21)
.... *Hemidactylus frenatus* (p. 76)
6   **A.** Middorsal zone of granular scales, sharply and distinctly differentiated from larger surrounding dorsal scales (Fig. 22) .... *Sphaerodactylus rosaurae* (p. 82)
    B. No distinct middorsal zone of granular scales, dorsal scales all subequal in size (Fig. 22) .... *Sphaerodactylus millepunctatus* (p. 80)

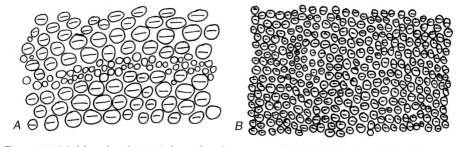

Figure 22. Middorsal scales in *Sphaerodactylus rosaurae* (SMF 81786; a) and *S. millepunctatus* (SMF 79212; b). Drawings by Philipp Groß.

7   **A.** Dorsal surface of head covered with granular scales; claws partially enclosed by sheaths (Fig. 21) .... *Coleonyx mitratus* (p. 74)
    B. Dorsal surface of head with enlarged plates or scales, never covered with granular scales; claws completely exposed, not covered by sheaths **8**
8   **A.** Venter covered with large squarish, juxtaposed, platelike scales or large, smooth, imbricate cycloid scales.. **9**
    B. Venter covered with small rounded, pointed, or granular scales, scales either smooth or keeled **11**
9   **A.** Body covered with small granular scales dorsally and large squarish, juxtaposed, platelike scales ventrally; femoral pores present, at least in males (Fig. 23)
.... *Cnemidophorus lemniscatus* (p. 120)
    B. Body covered by large uniform cycloid scales; femoral pores absent **10**

Figure 23. Ventral view of hind limbs and surrounding area in *Cnemidophorus lemniscatus* (SMF 79013) showing femoral pores. Drawing by Philipp Groß.

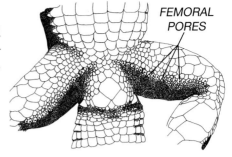

10 **A.** Paired supranasal (internasal) scales present (Fig. 18); two frontoparietal scales present (Fig. 18) .... *Mabuya unimarginata* (**p. 114**)

   B. Paired supranasal (internasal) scales absent; a single frontoparietal scale present ....*Sphenomorphus cherriei* (**p. 116**)

11 **A.** Femoral pores present (Fig. 23) 12

   B. Femoral pores absent 16

Figure 24. Side of head of *Iguana iguana* showing enlarged circular scale below tympanum. Drawing by Elke Köhler.

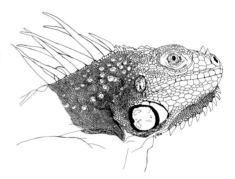

12 **A.** Tail with scales more or less uniform in size, not in conspicuous whorls; enlarged circular scale present on side of head below tympanum (Fig. 24) .... *Iguana iguana* (**p. 98**)

   B. Tail bearing whorls of enlarged spiny scales, separated by a row or rows of interwhorls (Fig. 25); no enlarged circular scale present on side of head below tympanum......... 13

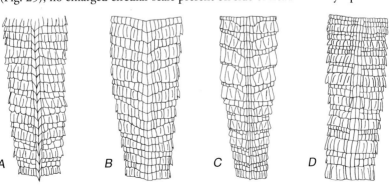

Figure 25. Dorsal view of *Ctenosaura* tails: (a) *Ctenosaura bakeri* (SMF 81059); (b) *C. melanosterna* (SMF 75508); (c) *C. oedirhina* (SMF 78036); (d) *C. similis* (SMF 82936). Drawings by Philipp Groß.

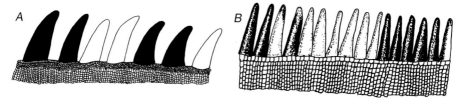

Figure 26. Dorsal spines of *Ctenosaura bakeri* (SMF 82646; a) and *C. similis* (SMF 11232; b). Drawings by Philipp Groß.

13 A. Middorsal crest consisting of 40 to 53 enlarged serrated scales (Fig. 26); dewlap well
　　　developed (Fig. 27) 14
　　B. Middorsal crest consisting of 60 or more enlarged serrated scales (Fig. 26); dewlap
　　　absent, but transverse fold present across throat 15

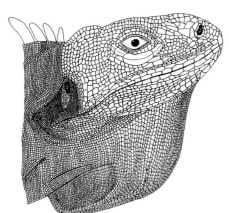

Figure 27. Lateral view of head of *Ctenosaura bakeri* showing dewlap. Drawing by Philipp Groß.

14 A. Intercalary rows of 8 or fewer caudal segments reduced to a single row dorsally (Fig.
　　　25) .... *Ctenosaura bakeri* (p. 90)
　　B. Intercalary rows of 12 or more caudal segments reduced to a single row dorsally (Fig.
　　　25) ....*Ctenosaura melanosterna* (p. 92)
15 A. Enlarged heavily keeled scales on dorsal surface of shank (Fig. 28); intercalary rows
　　　between tail whorls 3–5 reduced to a single row dorsally (Fig. 25)
　　　.. *Ctenosaura oedirhina* (p. 94)
　　B. Scales on dorsal surface of shank not enlarged and only slightly keeled (Fig. 28);
　　　scales in intercalary rows between tail whorls 3–5 in two rows dorsally (Fig. 25)
　　　.. *Ctenosaura similis* (p. 96)
16 A. Lateral flap of scales on outer edge of each hind toe (Fig. 29); adults with single-lobed
　　　cephalic crest (Fig. 30); no dewlap present .... *Basiliscus vittatus* (p. 87)
　　B. No lateral flap of scales on outer edge of each hind toe, lamellae widened (Fig. 29);
　　　no single-lobed cephalic crest present; dewlap present, at least in males (Fig. 31) 17

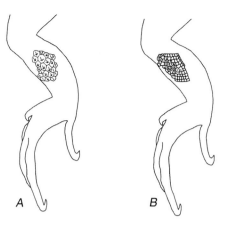

Figure 28. Shank scales of: (a) *Ctenosaura oedirhina* (SMF 78036) and (b) *Ctenosaura similis* (SMF 76000). Drawings by Gunther Köhler.

Figure 29. Ventral view of hind toe of *Basiliscus* (a) and *Norops* (b) showing lateral flap of scales and widened lamellae, respectively (shaded). Modified from Fig. 166 in Köhler (2003).

Figure 30. Head crest (shaded) of *Basiliscus vittatus*. Modified from Fig. 291 in Köhler (2003).

Figure 31. Photograph of male dewlap in a species of anole (*Norops lemurinus*). Photograph by Gunther Köhler

17 A. Dorsum of body primarily green in life; head turquoise blue; ear opening transversely elongate, with posterior margin forming a long longitudinal depression (Fig. 32); males with conspicuously large and elongate head (Fig. 32)
....*Anolis allisoni* (p. 100)
  B. Coloration not as above; ear opening vertically oval (Fig. 32) or oval, or, if elongate, no longitudinal depression on posterior margin; head of males not conspicuously large and elongate (Fig. 32) 18
18 A. Midventral scales at midbody smooth (Fig. 33) or obtusely keeled
.... *Norops utilensis* (p. 112)
  B. Midventral scales at midbody distinctly keeled (Fig. 33) 19

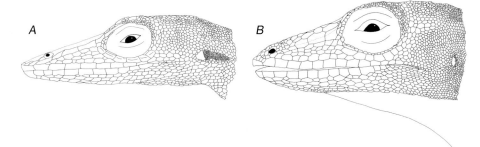

Figure 32. Lateral view of head of *Anolis allisoni* (SMF 78319; a) showing an elongate head and a transversely elongate ear opening with the posterior margin forming a long longitudinal depression and of *Norops utilensis* (SMF 79866; b) showing a vertically oval ear opening and a relatively short head. Drawings by Uta Imhoff.

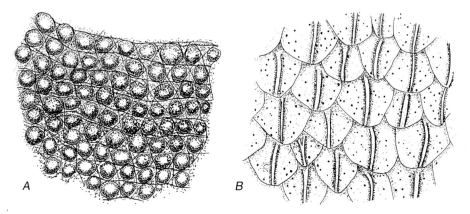

Figure 33. Smooth midventral scales in *Norops utilensis* (SMF 77983; a) and keeled midventral scales in *Norops sagrei* (SMF 77744; b). Drawings by Philipp Groß.

19 **A.** Outer postmental scale on each side greatly enlarged, length greater than length of mental scale (Fig. 34); four postmental scales .... *Norops sagrei* (**p. 108**)
    B. Outer postmental scale on each side not greatly enlarged, length much less than length of mental scale (Fig. 34); five or more postmental scales **20**

20 **A.** Short-legged (shank length/SVL usually <0.25; 4th toe of adpressed hind limb reaches usually to a point between shoulder and ear opening, in some individuals to between ear opening and eye); male dewlap yellowish orange with large deep blue or purple central spot ....*Norops sericeus* (**p. 110**)
    B. Long-legged (shank length/SVL usually >0.25; 4th toe of adpressed hind limb reaches at least to posterior border of eye); male dewlap color not as above...................... **21**

21 **A.** Male dewlap pinkish orange to reddish orange, without suffusion of black pigment, often with black gorgetal scales; maximum SVL 68 mm in males, 79 mm in females
    .... *Norops lemurinus* (**p. 104**)
    B. Dewlap reddish orange to pinkish red, with central suffusion of black pigment, gorgetal scales white; maximum SVL variable.. **22**

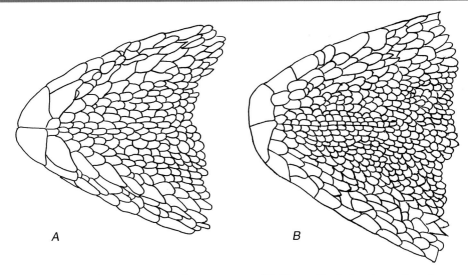

Figure 34. Ventral view of snout of *Norops sagrei* (SMF 77743; a) showing enlarged outer postmental scale and that of *N. bicaorum* (SMF 77102; b) showing outer postmental scale not enlarged. Drawings by Philipp Groß.

22 A. Dewlap reddish orange; maximum SVL 75 mm in males, 67 mm in female .... *Norops bicaorum* (**p. 102**)

B. Dewlap pinkish red; maximum SVL 62 mm in males, 63 mm in females ....*Norops roatanensis* (**p. 106**)

Family Eublepharidae

Species of the family Eublepharidae are covered dorsally by small, granular scales, have skin that is fragile and tears easily, and have moveable eyelids. Most members of this family lack the subdigital setae found in many members of the family Gekkonidae (Pough et al., 2003). This family of lizards is disjunctly distributed circumglobally in tropical and some temperate areas. In the Western Hemisphere, it is disjunctly distributed from the southwestern United States (southern California, southern Nevada, southwestern Utah, western and southern Arizona, southern New Mexico, and southwestern to south-central Texas) southward into Baja California and northwestern and north-central to northeastern mainland Mexico, southern Mexico, and Central America south to south-central Costa Rica. In the Eastern Hemisphere, the family is disjunctly distributed in eastern and western tropical Africa, from eastern Iraq to eastern India, southern Thailand through Sarawak and Borneo to Sanana Island, and the Ryu Kyu Islands of Japan and islands in the Gulf of Tonkin, China. Six genera comprised of 22 species are currently included in this family (Grismer, 1988; Rösler, 2000). One species is known to occur in Honduras, including the Bay Islands.

Coleonyx mitratus (W. Peters, 1863)

Common name(s): Banded Gecko (English*).

Description: *Coleonyx mitratus* is a moderately-sized gecko (males to 91 mm SVL, females to 97 mm [Savage, 2002]) with a relatively short tail (about 1.0 to 1.2 times SVL). The head is covered with a mixture of small granular scales and larger tubercles and the eyes are large, with vertically elliptical pupils. Moveable eyelids are present. Dorsal body scales are granular with larger tubercles interspersed among the granular scales. Ventral scales are smooth, flat, and imbricate. Limbs are short and stocky and digits lack expanded pads and have 16 to 18 undivided subdigital lamellae on Digit IV of the hind limbs. The claws are partially or entirely hidden by two shell-like lateral scales. The median subcaudal scales are enlarged and in 1 or 2 rows. Precloacal pores number 5 to 9 in males only, although females possess analogous pits. Dorsal surfaces are some shade of brown, with dark brown outlined pale brown crossbands on the body. Ventral surfaces are uniformly cream.

Similar species: All members of the related Family Gekkonidae on the Islas de la Bahía lack eyelids, having instead a transparent spectacle covering the eye.

General geographic distribution: Low and moderate elevations from extreme eastern Guatemala to central Costa Rica on the Atlantic versant and from southeastern Guatemala to south-central Costa Rica on the Pacific versant.

Distribution on Las Islas de la Bahía: *Coleonyx mitratus* is only known from Utila.

Natural history comments: *Coleonyx mitratus* is nocturnal and terrestrial; most individuals are seen walking on the ground. We collected this species on Utila in May and October. Habitat types on the Bay Islands include hardwood forest and urban areas.

Coleonyx mitratus from Isla de Utila.
Photograph by Robert Powell

Coleonyx mitratus from Isla de Utila.
Photograph by James R. McCranie

Coleonyx mitratus from Isla de Utila.
Photograph by Robert Powell

Coleonyx mitratus from Isla de Utila.
Photograph by Gunther Köhler

Family Gekkonidae

Species of the family Gekkonidae (following the classification of Kluge, 1987) are covered dorsally by small granular scales, have skin that is fragile and tears easily, and lack moveable eyelids. Many species have greatly expanded subdigital toe pads containing setae that allow for exceptional climbing abilities. One lineage (containing *Sphaerodactylus* on the Bay Islands) has expanded subdigital lamellae, but lack the greatly expanded toe pads, although they still retain good climbing abilities. Gekkonids are found in the Western Hemisphere from southern California, USA, to the southern tip of Baja California, Mexico, and from Sonora and Veracruz, Mexico, southward to Chile and southern Argentina. They also occur on the Galápagos Islands, in southeastern Florida, USA, the Bahama Islands, the Greater and Lesser Antilles, Trinidad and Tobago, and on many islands along both coasts of Middle America. They range throughout the Eastern Hemisphere south of about 42°N latitude to the southern tips of Africa, Australia, and New Zealand. A number of gecko species have been widely introduced to tropical and sub-tropical environments around the world, including Honduras. About 75 genera containing 800+ species are said to be in this family (Pough et al., 2003; their subfamily Gekkoninae). Six genera comprising 14 species are currently known to occupy Honduran territory, with four genera containing five species known to occur on the Islas de la Bahía.

Hemidactylus frenatus Schlegel, *in* Duméril and Bibron, 1836

Common name(s): House Gecko (English*); Geco (Spanish).

Description: *Hemidactylus frenatus* is a moderately-sized gecko (males to 65 mm SVL, females to 60 mm) with a relatively short tail (about 1.0 to 1.2 times SVL). The eyes are large, with vertical pupils. Moveable eyelids are absent. Head and dorsal body scales are granular, with some enlarged, weakly keeled scales scattered among the granules on the body. Ventral scales are smooth, imbricate, and much larger than the dorsal scales. Limbs are short and stocky. Digits lack basal webbing, and 9 or 10 expanded, medially divided, subdigital lamellae are present on Digit IV of the hind limb. The claw is terminally located on each digit and is nonretractable. The tail is flattened, with 6 longitudinal rows of enlarged, keeled tubercles. These rows of enlarged tubercles are separated by 8 rows of smooth scales. The median row of subcaudal scales is enlarged and platelike. About 25 to 36 total femoral

Hemidactylus frenatus from the Honduran mainland. Photograph by James R. McCranie

Hemidactylus frenatus from Isla de Utila.
Photograph by Breck Bartholomew

and precloacal pores are present in males, but these pores are absent in females. Dorsal coloration varies from day to night. Nighttime color can be buff, pinkish-tan, tan, or brown with scattered dark spots. Daytime color tends to be darker. The ventral surface is uniformly creamy white, yellow, or tan.

Similar species: *Hemidactylus frenatus* differs from all other geckos known from the Islas de la Bahía (except *Phyllodactylus palmeus* and *Thecadactylus rapicauda*) by having medially divided subdigital lamellae on the toe pads. *Phyllodactylus palmeus* has the distal pair of subdigital lamellae expanded to form leaflike pads. *Thecadactylus rapicauda* has 12 to 25 subdigital lamellae on Digit IV of the hind limb, basal webbing between the digits, a retractable claw, and a larger size (adults reach 126 mm SVL).

General geographic distribution: "Taiwan, Hong Kong, Guangdong, Hainan, and southern Yunnan, China. Southern and eastern Africa, Madagascar, Mauritius, south and southeastern Asia, Philippines, Japan (Ryukyu and Bonin islands), Indoaustralian Archipelago east to New Guinea and northern Australia; Oceania and Mexico. Introduced into Mariana Islands (Guam) and USA (Hawaiian Islands)" (Zhao and Adler, 1993:184). Also widely introduced in Central America, and introduced populations have also been reported from Florida and Texas, USA.

Distribution on Las Islas de la Bahía: *Hemidactylus frenatus* has been introduced on Utila.

Natural history comments: *Hemidactylus frenatus* occurs in edificarian situations on the Bay Islands, and numerous individuals can be seen moving across walls of buildings at night. These geckos have a voice and frequently squeak while active. The species is likely to be introduced to other islands in Las Islas de la Bahía in the near future. Certainly, on the Honduran mainland, this gecko is rapidly expanding its distribution.

Phyllodactylus palmeus Dixon, 1968

Common name(s): Chumpatia (probably corrupted Spanish).

Description: *Phyllodactylus palmeus* is a moderately-sized gecko (males to 76 mm SVL, females to 69 mm [Dixon, 1968]) with a relatively short tail (about 1.0 to 1.4 times SVL). The head is covered with a mixture of small granular scales and larger tubercles. Eyes are large, with vertically elliptical pupils. Moveable eyelids are absent. Dorsal body scales are granular, but are intermixed with enlarged and keeled scales arranged in longitudinal rows. Ventral scales are smooth and imbricate. Limbs are short and stocky. Digits lack basal webbing and 13 to 15 single (except for the enlarged terminal pair) subdigital lamellae are present on Digit IV of the hind limbs. A terminal pair of subdigital lamellae forming an enlarged leaf-like pad is present on each digit. The claw is terminally located on each digit and is nonretractable. The tail has 6 to 8 longitudinal rows of enlarged, keeled tubercles basally. The median subcaudal scales are enlarged and in 1 or 2 (mostly 1) rows. Femoral and precloacal pores are absent. Dorsal surfaces of the head and body have a ground color of pale brownish gray or pale brown. The dorsal body pattern varies from darker brown crossbands to a darker brown tessellated pattern. Ventral surfaces are uniformly creamy white.

Similar species: *Coleonyx mitratus* has moveable eyelids. *Sphaerodactylus millepunctatus* and *S. rosaurae* have single lamellae beneath the toes. *Hemidactylus frenatus* has 9 or 10 expanded, medially divided, subdigital lamellae on Digit IV of the hind limb. *Thecadactylus rapicauda* has more than 12 divided subdigital lamellae on Digit IV of the hands and feet, with the distalmost widely separated by skin.

General geographic distribution: *Phyllodactylus palmeus* is endemic to the Bay Islands and Cayos Cochinos.

Distribution on Las Islas de la Bahía: The species occurs on Barbareta, Guanaja, Morat, Roatán, Utila, Cayo Cochino Grande, and Cayo Cochino Pequeño.

Natural history comments: *Phyllodactylus palmeus* is a nocturnal species that frequently occurs on walls of buildings. It also has been found active on rock walls inside a cave, on coconut palm trunks, and on thorn palm trunks. During the day, it has been found while inactive in termite nests, in holes in mangrove trees, beneath tree bark, and in rotting logs and other debris on the ground. *Phyllodactylus palmeus* is apparently active throughout the year. Habitat types on the Bay Islands and the Cayos Cochinos include hardwood forest, pine forest, mangrove forest, coconut groves (and various beach vegetation zones), and urban areas.

Phyllodactylus palmeus from Isla de Roatán.
Photograph by James R. McCranie

Phyllodactylus palmeus from Cayo Cochino Pequeño. Photograph by Mikael Lundberg

Phyllodactylus palmeus from Cayo Cochino Pequeño. Photograph by Mikael Lundberg

Phyllodactylus palmeus from Isla de Roatán. Photograph by James R. McCranie.
Inset: *Phyllodactylus palmeus* communal nest site from Islas de Utila. Photograph by Breck Bartholomew

Sphaerodactylus millepunctatus Hallowell, "1860" (1861)

Common name(s): Woodslave (English); Escupion (probably corrupted Spanish).

Description: *Sphaerodactylus millepunctatus* is a small gecko (males to 30 mm SVL, females to 31 mm) with a relatively short tail (about 0.9 to 1.0 times SVL). The head is covered with small granular scales. Eyes are small with nearly round pupils. Moveable eyelids are absent. Dorsal body scales are oval, keeled, and imbricate. Ventral scales are round, smooth, imbricate, and are larger than the dorsals. The median subcaudal scales are greatly enlarged, forming a continuous longitudinal row. Adult males have enlarged escutcheon scales on the venter and usually on the undersides of the thighs. Digits lack expanded pads, are dorsolaterally compressed at the distal end, and have 9 to 13 undivided subdigital lamellae on Digit IV of the hind limb. Claws are retractable and are displaced laterally between an enlarged terminal pilose pad and several smaller terminal scales. Femoral and precloacal pores are absent. Adults are brown with small darker brown spots dorsally on the body and usually dark brown lines and spots on the head. Dark sacral and nuchal spots or bands are present in juveniles; these markings can be retained into adulthood, but usually are lost in larger individuals.

Similar species: *Coleonyx mitratus* has moveable eyelids. *Hemidactylus frenatus, Phyllodactylus palmeus,* and *Thecadactylus rapicauda* have greatly expanded subdigital toe pads with divided lamellae. *Sphaerodactylus rosaurae* has a middorsal zone of granular scales, sharply and distinctly differentiated from the larger dorsal scales on either side.

General geographic distribution: Low and moderate elevations from the Isthmus of Tehuantepec and northern Oaxaca, Mexico, to northern Costa Rica on the Atlantic versant and northwestern Costa Rica on the Pacific versant. In addition to the Bay Islands, it also occurs on Isla Cozumel, Mexico, and Isla Maíz Grande, Nicaragua.

Distribution on Las Islas de la Bahía: *Sphaerodactylus millepunctatus* occurs on Barbareta, Guanaja, Morat, Roatán, and Utila.

Sphaerodactylus millepunctatus from Isla de Roatán. Photograph by James R. McCranie

Sphaerodactylus millepunctatus from Isla de Roatán. Photograph by James R. McCranie

Natural history comments: *Sphaerodactylus millepunctatus* is primarily diurnal and active in leaf litter and other debris on the ground. It is also occasionally seen inside houses. The species also has been seen in a building on Utila while actively feeding at night on insects attracted to a light. *Sphaerodactylus millepunctatus* is probably active throughout the year on the Bay Islands. Habitat types on the Bay Islands include hardwood forest, coconut groves (and various beach vegetation zones), and urban areas.

Remarks: L. Wilson and Hahn (1973) included this species under the name *Sphaerodactylus continentalis*.

Sphaerodactylus millipunctatus from Isla de Utila. Photograph by Gunther Köhler

Sphaerodactylus rosaurae Parker, 1940

Common name(s): Woodslave (English); Chumpatia (probably corrupted Spanish); Escupion (probably corrupted Spanish).

Description: *Sphaerodactylus rosaurae* is a small gecko (males to 38 mm SVL, females to 39 mm) with a relatively short tail (about 0.8 to 1.0 times SVL). The head is covered with small granular scales. Eyes are small, with nearly round pupils. Moveable eyelids are absent. Dorsal body scales are large, oval or rounded, and nonimbricate to slightly imbricate; these enlarged dorsal scales are divided medially by a narrow middorsal zone (1 or 2 rows) of granular scales. Ventral scales are smooth and imbricate. Adult males have enlarged escutcheon scales on the venter. Digits lack expanded pads, are dorsally compressed at the distal end, and have 10 to 15 undivided subdigital lamellae on Digit IV of the hind limbs. Claws are retractable and are displaced laterally between an enlarged terminal pilose pad and several smaller terminal scales. The median subcaudal scales are greatly enlarged and in a single row distal to the basal area. Femoral and precloacal pores are absent. Adults are strongly dichromatic in color. Adult males have the dorsal surfaces of the body essentially uniformly pale olive-green to gray and the top of the head has black spots; however, those spots are lost in the largest individuals. Adult females have an olive-green dorsum with scattered black flecks and a pale olive-green head with scattered rust-red flecks. The dorsal surface of the body of juveniles is yellowish green with black crossbands.

Similar species: *Coleonyx mitratus* has moveable eyelids. *Hemidactylus frenatus*, *Phyllodactylus palmeus*, and *Thecadactylus rapicauda* have greatly expanded subdigital toe pads with divided lamellae. *Sphaerodactylus millepunctatus* has no distinct middorsal zone of granular scales, the dorsal scales all being subequal in size.

General geographic distribution: *Sphaerodactylus rosaurae* is endemic to the Bay Islands.

Distribution on Las Islas de la Bahía: The species occurs on Barbareta, Guanaja, Morat, Roatán, and Utila.

Sphaerodactylus rosaurae adult from Isla de Roatán. Photograph by James R. McCranie

Sphaerodactylus rosaurae juvenile from Isla de Roatán. Photograph by James R. McCranie

Natural history comments: *Sphaerodactylus rosaurae* is a diurnal species that is active in leaf litter and other ground debris, as well as on the lower portions of trunks of mangrove trees. It occurs on sandy beaches, as well as in the forested interior. L. Wilson and Hahn (1973:109) reported that specimens of this species were collected from "stilt rootlets of coconut palm stumps, under rotting palm logs, inside hollow standing thorn palms, under palm fronds, in the axils of fronds on coconut palms, in crevices of rock coral, in abandoned thatched huts, and under rocks." The species is probably active throughout the year. Habitat types on the Bay Islands include hardwood forest, mangrove forest, and coconut groves (including various beach area vegetation zones).

Sphaerodactylus rosaurae from Isla de Roatán. Photograph by James R. McCranie

Thecadactylus rapicauda (Houttuyn, 1782)

Common name(s): Turniptail Gecko (English; Liner, 1994).

Description: *Thecadactylus rapicauda* is the largest gecko found on the Islas de la Bahía (males to 125 mm SVL, females to 126 mm [Russell and Bauer, 2002]) with a relatively short tail (about 0.6 to 0.9 times SVL). Eyes are large with vertically elliptical pupils. Movable eyelids are absent. Dorsal scales of the head and body are small, uniform, and granular. Ventral scales are round to oval, imbricate, smooth, and are larger than the dorsal scales. Subcaudal scales are squarish, flat, and larger than the ventral scales. Limbs are short and stocky. Digits have large expanded toe pads and are basally webbed, with 14 to 25 medially divided subdigital lamellae on Digit IV of the hind limb. The claw is retractable into a fleshy sulcus. The tail is easily lost and most adults have regenerated tails that have the proximal part fleshy and much wider than the base of the tail, and the distal part tapering to a blunt tip. Femoral and precloacal pores are absent. Coloration is highly variable and can change with fluctuations in environmental or physiological conditions. Dorsal body and tail coloration can range from creamy white to different shades of gray or brown, or even black, and can possess a number of different dorsal patterns, including chevrons, spots, or bars. Ventral surfaces are creamy white or beige.

Similar species: The only other gecko on the Islas de la Bahía with greatly expanded subdigital toe pads with divided lamellae is *Hemidactylus frenatus*. *Hemidactylus frenatus* does not exceed 65 mm SVL, lacks basal webbing between the digits, and has a non-retractable terminal claw on each toe, and 9 or 10 subdigital lamellae on Digit IV of the hind limb.

General geographic distribution: *Thecadactylus rapicauda* has the most extensive natural range of any New World gecko (Russell and Bauer, 2002). It occurs at low and moderate elevations from the outer end of the Yucatán Peninsula and Chiapas, Mexico, to Bolivia, and much of Amazonian Brazil on the Atlantic versant and from Costa Rica to Ecuador on the Pacific versant. It also occurs through the Lesser Antilles and on Trinidad and Tobago, Islas del Maíz, Nicaragua, and Islas de las Perlas, Panamá.

Distribution on Las Islas de la Bahía: *Thecadactylus rapicauda* is recorded only from Utila.

Natural history comments: *Thecadactylus rapicauda* is a nocturnal species that has been found active on or in buildings, on tree trunks, and in rock outcrops on mainland Honduras. One individual was found inactive during the day inside an abandoned thatch-roofed building in a clearing in hardwood forest on Utila. The species is probably active year round on Utila.

Thecadactylus rapicauda from Isla de Utila. Photograph by Robert Powell.

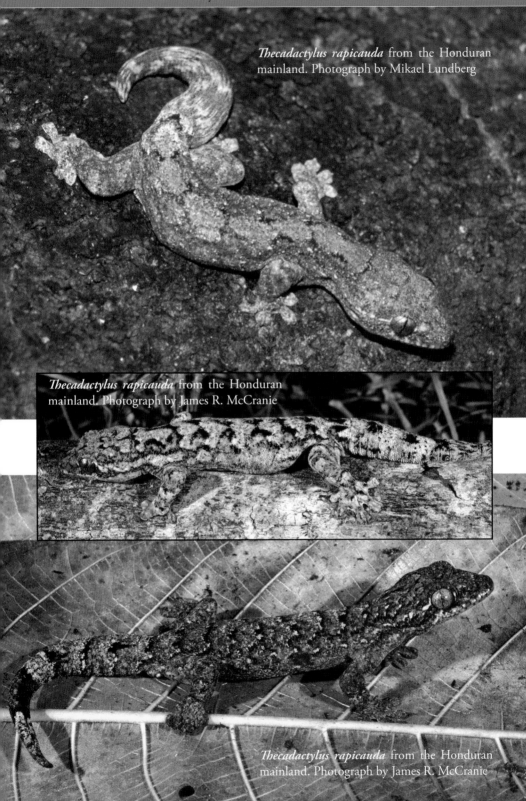

Thecadactylus rapicauda from the Honduran mainland. Photograph by Mikael Lundberg

Thecadactylus rapicauda from the Honduran mainland. Photograph by James R. McCranie

Thecadactylus rapicauda from the Honduran mainland. Photograph by James R. McCranie

Family Corytophanidae

Corytophanid lizards (we follow Frost and Etheridge, 1989, and Frost et al., 2001, in recognizing familial status for these lizards; for a different view, see Schulte et al., 2003) are characterized by the presence of well-developed head crests or casques (Pough et al., 2003, who recognize this group as a subfamily within the Iguanidae). These crests or casques are sexually dimorphic in the genus *Basiliscus* (well developed only in males), whereas they are equally developed in both sexes of the other genera. The members of this family are limited in distribution to the Western Hemisphere, within which they range from Tamaulipas and Jalisco, Mexico, southward through Central America into South America as far south as west-central Venezuela east of the Andes and western Ecuador west of the Andes. Three genera comprised of nine species are currently included in this family (Pough et al., 2003). All three genera, including seven species, are known to occupy Honduras. One species occurs on the Islas de la Bahía.

Basiliscus vittatus adult male from Isla de Utila. Photograph by Naturfoto-Kornacker

Basiliscus vittatus Wiegmann, 1828

Common name(s): Monkey Lala (English); Black Lizard (English); Pichete Monterudo (Spanish).

Description: This moderately large lizard (males to 170 mm SVL, females to 134 mm) has a very long tail (about 2.3 to 3.2 times SVL). Adult males have a single lobed, laterally compressed head crest. The head crest of adult females consists of a small knob on the posterior portion of the head. The tympanum is distinct and higher than long. An enlarged scale below the tympanic region is lacking. Supralabials number 7 or 8 and the infralabials 7 to 9. Dorsal body scales are keeled and imbricate. Adult males have a raised middorsal crest that is supported by bony rays in larger individuals; females and subadult males have a middorsal crest consisting of a row of serrated scales. Adults of both sexes have a low, serrated dorsal caudal keel. Ventral scales are keeled and imbricate. Caudal autotomy is absent, as are femoral and precloacal pores. A lateral flap of scales is present on the outer edge of each hind toe. Dorsal ground color is usually pale brown to dark brown; darker brown crossbands are usually present in females. A pair of pale brown dorsolateral stripes is usually present. Ventral surfaces are tan to gray with some pinkish orange to orange pigment. The iris is orange to brown.

Similar species: No other lizard on the Islas de la Bahía has a well-developed, elevated crest on the head of adult males. Juvenile and female basilisks might be confused with some of the anole species, but all anoles in the region have a dewlap (best developed in adult males) and expanded subdigital pads, and lack a lateral flap of scales on the outer edges of the hind toes.

General geographic distribution: Low and moderate elevations from southern Tamaulipas, Mexico, to northwestern Colombia on the Atlantic versant and from northwestern Jalisco, Mexico, to west-central Nicaragua and from central Panamá to northwestern Colombia on the Pacific versant. It has also been introduced into southern Florida, USA.

Basiliscus vittatus adult female from the Honduran mainland. Photograph by James R. McCranie

Distribution on Las Islas de la Bahía: *Basiliscus vittatus* occurs on Barbareta, Guanaja, Roatán, Utila, and Cayo Cochino Grande.

Natural history comments: *Basiliscus vittatus* is a diurnal species that can be abundant in many areas on the Islas de la Bahía. Adults are primarily arboreal, being found in trees and shrubs, whereas juveniles are primarily terrestrial. The species occurs in both riparian and nonriparian situations and is probably active throughout the year. *Basiliscus vittatus* is capable of bipedal locomotion (using only its two hind limbs) across the surface of water, and uses this method of locomotion to escape from potential predators. Habitat types on the Islas de la Bahía include hardwood forest, pine forest, mangrove forest, coconut groves (including beach area vegetation), ironshore formations, swamps and marshes, and urban areas.

Basiliscus vittatus subadult from Isla de Utila. Photograph by Robert Powell

Family Iguanidae

Iguanids are generally moderately-sized to large terrestrial, rock-dwelling, or arboreal, primarily herbivorous lizards (Pough et al., 2003, who also recognize this group as a subfamily within the Iguanidae). We follow Frost and Etheridge (1989) and Frost et al. (2001) in the recognition of the family Iguanidae; see Schulte et al. (2003) for a conflicting opinion. The Islas de la Bahía species of this family are the largest lizards on these islands. Family members range in the Western Hemisphere from southeastern California, southern Nevada, and southwestern and south-central Utah in the USA, southward to the southern tip of the Baja California Peninsula (excepting the northwestern sector), the coastlands of western Mexico, and Tamaulipas, Mexico, thence southward through Central America into South America as far south as Ecuador west of the Andes and southeastern Brazil east of the Andes. They also occur on the Bahama Islands, Cuba, Jamaica, Hispaniola, the Cayman Islands, Mona Island, the Lesser Antilles, and the Galápagos Islands. The family has also been introduced into southern Florida, USA. In the Eastern Hemisphere, they are distributed on the Fiji and Tonga Islands in the southwestern Pacific Ocean. The family is composed of eight genera (Pough et al., 2003) comprised of about 43 species. Two genera containing six species are known to occupy Honduras, of which both genera and five species occur on the Islas de la Bahía. Two of the species of *Ctenosaura* are endemic to the Bay Islands.

Ctenosaura similis from Isla de Utila.
Photograph by Naturfoto-Kornacker

Ctenosaura bakeri Stejneger, 1901

Common name(s): Swamper, Utila Iguana (English).

Description: This large and heavy bodied lizard (males to 315 mm SVL, females to 230 mm) has a long tail (about 1.5 to 1.7 times SVL). Head crests or casques are absent. The tympanum is distinct and higher than long, and there is no very enlarged scale below the tympanic region. A large pendulous dewlap is present. Nine to 13 supralabials and 9 to 12 infralabials are present. Dorsal body scales are variable and can be granular, smooth, or slightly keeled on the same individual. A distinct middorsal crest consisting of 40 to 53 enlarged serrated scales is present; this crest is best developed in adult males. Ventral scales are smooth and imbricate. The tail has whorls of large spinous scales and intercalary scales between the whorls. One complete row of intercalary scales is present between the third and fifth tail whorls, with 8 or fewer total intercalary caudal segments reduced to a single row dorsally. Caudal autotomy is absent. Fourteen to 22 total femoral pores are present. Scales on the anterodorsal surface of the shank are enlarged. Adults have a dorsal head and body ground color of brown or gray, with or without 4 to 6 indistinct darker crossbands present on the body. Juveniles have olive-green, pale brown, or dark brown dorsal surfaces, usually with a few, incomplete brown to black crossbands on the body.

Similar species: *Iguana iguana* has a tail with scales more or less uniform in size and an enlarged circular scale present on the side of the head below the tympanum. *Ctenosaura oedirhina* and *C. similis* have 60 or more enlarged median dorsal crest scales and lack a dewlap. *Ctenosaura oedirhina* also usually has 3 to 5 pale crossbands on the body. *Ctenosaura similis* also has two complete rows of intercalary scales present between the third and fifth tail whorls and scales on the anterodorsal surface of the shank that are not enlarged. *Ctenosaura melanosterna* has 12 or more caudal segments of intercalary rows reduced to a single row dorsally.

Ctenosaura bakeri adult male from Isla de Utila. Photograph by Wolf Steiger.

Ctenosaura bakeri adult male from Isla de Utila. Photograph by Gunther Köhler

General geographic distribution: *Ctenosaura bakeri* is endemic to Utila.

Distribution on Las Islas de la Bahía: See General geographic distribution.

Natural history comments: *Ctenosaura bakeri* is a diurnal, arboreal species that occurs in mangrove swamps. Retreats of this species are located in hollow sections of mangrove trees. Females move to sandy areas of beach margin forest and coconut groves to lay their eggs. People on Utila eat the meat and eggs of this species; thus, populations of this lizard are in jeopardy. Also, pristine sections of beach are critical for the females to lay their eggs. Without these nesting beaches, *C. bakeri* populations will quickly decline (also see the section on Conservation Efforts).

Ctenosaura bakeri adult female from Isla de Utila. Photograph by Gunther Köhler

Ctenosaura melanosterna **Buckley and Axtell, 1997**

Common name(s): Spinytail Iguana (English*).

Description: This large and heavy bodied lizard (males to 320 mm SVL, females to 232 mm [Buckley and Axtell, 1997]) has a long tail (about 1.3 to 1.7 times SVL). Head crests or casques are absent. The tympanum is distinct and higher than long. An enlarged scale below the tympanic region is lacking. A large pendulous dewlap is present. Eight to 11 supralabials and 9 to 12 infralabials are present. Dorsal body scales are variable and can be granular, smooth, or slightly keeled on the same individual. A distinct middorsal crest consisting of 41 to 52 enlarged serrated scales is present; this crest is best developed in adult males. Ventral scales are smooth and imbricate. The tail has whorls of large spinous scales and intercalary scales between the whorls. One complete row of intercalary scales is present between the third and fifth tail whorls, with 12 or more total intercalary caudal segments reduced to a single row dorsally. Caudal autotomy is absent. Twelve to 22 total femoral pores are present. Scales on the anterodorsal surface of the shank are enlarged. Adults have a dorsal head and body ground color of some shade of pale brown or olive-green, with 3 to 5 darker crossbands present on the body; these crossbands diminish in intensity posteriorly. Juveniles have a dorsal ground color of gray to olive-green, with darker crossbands on the body.

Similar species: *Iguana iguana* has a tail with scales more or less uniform in size and an enlarged circular scale present on the side of the head below the tympanum. *Ctenosaura oedirhina* and *C. similis* have 60 or more enlarged median dorsal crest scales and lack a dewlap. *Ctenosaura oedirhina* also usually has 3 to 5 pale crossbands on the body. *Ctenosaura*

Ctenosaura melanosterna adult male from Cayo Cochino Pequeño. Photograph by Mikael Lundberg

Ctenosaura melanosterna from Cayo Cochino Pequeño. Photograph by Mikael Lundberg

similis also has 2 complete rows of intercalary scales present between the third and fifth tail whorls and scales on the anterodorsal surface of the shank that are not enlarged. *Ctenosaura bakeri* has 8 or fewer caudal segments of intercalary rows reduced to a single row dorsally.

General geographic distribution: Low elevations on the Atlantic versant in the middle portion of the Río Aguan Valley in north-central Honduras and on the Cayos Cochinos.

Distribution on Las Islas de la Bahía: *Ctenosaura melanosterna* is recorded from Cayo Cochino Grande and Cayo Cochino Pequeño.

Natural history comments: The following was extracted from L. Wilson and Cruz Díaz (1993:17): "On Cochino Grande, lizards were seen in the vicinity of a half-constructed house. One specimen was collected from beneath a pile of concrete blocks, the other two from the walls of the buildings. One specimen escaped by climbing a tree. On Cochino Pequeño, a young ctenosaur was seen in hill forest and another two on the isthmus behind Bonkes Nose Point. An adult ctenosaur was seen on a steep rocky cliff face along the shore of the island." Habitat types on the Cayos Cochinos include hardwood forest and ironshore formations.

Remarks: *Ctenosaura melanosterna* was included under the name *C. palearis* in L. Wilson and Cruz Díaz (1993).

Ctenosaura melanosterna from the Honduran mainland. Photograph by James R. McCranie

Ctenosaura oedirhina De Queiroz, 1987

Common name(s): Bushwilly, Witchwilly, Wishwilly (English); Garrobo (Spanish).

Description: This large and heavy bodied lizard (males to 270 mm SVL, females to about 200 mm [but see Remarks]) has a long tail (about 1.6 to 2.2 times SVL). Head crests or casques are absent. The tympanum is distinct and higher than long. An enlarged scale below the tympanic region is lacking. A large pendulous dewlap is absent. Eight to 11 supralabials and 9 to 11 infralabials are present. Dorsal body scales are variable and can be granular, smooth, or slightly keeled on the same individual. A low middorsal crest consisting of more than 60 enlarged serrated scales is present; this crest is best developed in adult males. Ventral scales are smooth and slightly imbricate. The tail has whorls of large spinous scales and intercalary scales between the whorls. One complete row of intercalary scales is present between the third and fifth tail whorls, with at least 10 total intercalary segments with a single row dorsally. Caudal autotomy is absent. Eighteen to 30 total femoral pores are present. Scales on the anterodorsal surface of the shank are enlarged. Adults have a dorsal head and body ground color of dark gray to black, with 3 to 5 pale (orangish white to cream) crossbands present on the body. Juveniles have green dorsal surfaces, usually with a few, incomplete brown to black crossbands on the body.

Similar species: *Iguana iguana* has a tail with scales more or less uniform in size and an enlarged circular scale present on the side of the head below the tympanum. *Ctenosaura bakeri* and *C. melanosterna* have 53 or fewer enlarged median dorsal crest scales and a distinct dewlap. *Ctenosaura similis* has distinct dark crossbands on the body, keeled (but not enlarged and spinous) scales on the anterodorsal surface of the shank, and 2 complete rows of intercalary scales between the third and fifth tail whorls.

General geographic distribution: *Ctenosaura oedirhina* is endemic to Roatán and two nearby islands.

Ctenosaura oedirhina adult female from Isla de Roatán. Photograph by James R. McCranie.

Ctenosaura oedirhina subadult from Isla de Barbareta. Photograph by James R. McCranie

Distribution on Las Islas de la Bahía: The species occurs on Roatán and Barbareta (and nearby Big Pigeon Cay).

Natural history comments: *Ctenosaura oedirhina* is a diurnal, arboreal and terrestrial species. It can be seen on the ground in open sandy areas (including beaches), on the ground in rocky areas, on buildings, in trees, and on rock cliffs. Kaiser et al. (2001a) reported vocal communication in this species on eastern Roatán. This species is probably active throughout the year. Some people on Roatán use *Ctenosaura oedirhina* as a source of protein. Habitat types include hardwood forest, mangrove forest, coconut groves (including various beach area zones), and ironshore formations.

Remarks: *Ctenosaura oedirhina* was included under the name *C. bakeri* by L. Wilson and Hahn (1973). *Ctenosaura oedirhina* can reach a considerably larger size than what has been recorded in the literature. Adults of both sexes that appeared much larger than the maximum-recorded SVL for the species were seen around the house of one of the private owners of Isla Barbareta in February 1990 (McCranie pers. observ.). Köhler (1995) estimated a SVL of 350 mm for some individuals in this population. These *Ctenosaura* are afforded protection by the landowner; thus, these adults are apparently able to reach a larger size than those individuals under hunting pressure.

Ctenosaura oedirhina adult female from Isla de Roatán. Photograph by Breck Bartholomew

Ctenosaura similis (Gray, 1831)

Common name(s): Bushwilly, Witchwilly, Wishwilly (English); Garrobo (Spanish).

Description: This very large and heavy bodied lizard (males to 490 mm SVL, females to 400 mm) has a long tail (about 1.5 to 2.4 times SVL, proportionally longer in juveniles). Head crests or casques are absent. The tympanum is distinct and higher than long. An enlarged scale below the tympanic region is lacking. A large pendulous dewlap is absent. Supralabials and infralabials number 10 to 15. Dorsal body scales are variable and can be granular, smooth, or slightly keeled on the same individual. A distinct middorsal crest consisting of 61 to 96 enlarged serrated scales is present; this crest is best developed in adult males. Ventral scales are smooth and imbricate. The tail has whorls of large spinous scales and intercalary scales between the whorls. Two complete rows of intercalary scales are present between all but the anterior 1 to 2 tail whorls. Caudal autotomy is absent. Six to 18 total femoral pores are present. Scales on the anterodorsal surface of the shank are not enlarged. Adults have a dorsal head and body ground color of pale brown, tan, or gray (or various colors in between), with 4 to 6 darker crossbands present on the body. Juveniles have green dorsal surfaces, usually with a few, incomplete brown to black crossbands on the body.

Similar species: *Iguana iguana* has a tail with scales more or less uniform in size and an enlarged circular scale present on the side of the head below the tympanum. *Ctenosaura bakeri* and *C. melanosterna* have 50 or fewer enlarged median dorsal crest scales and a distinct dewlap. *Ctenosaura oedirhina* has a patch of enlarged and spinous scales on the anterodorsal surface of the shank, a single row of intercalary scales between the third and fifth tail whorls, and pale crossbands on the body.

General geographic distribution: Low and moderate elevations on the Atlantic versant from central Tabasco and the Yucatán Peninsula, Mexico, to northeastern Honduras and in western Nicaragua, eastern Costa Rica, and central Panamá (including numerous islands in the Caribbean Sea) and from southeastern Oaxaca, Mexico, to west-central Panamá on the Pacific versant (including several islands

Ctenosaura similis from Isla de Guanaja.
Photograph by Gunther Köhler

Ctenosaura similis subadult from Isla de Guanaja. Photograph by James R. McCranie

near the coast). It has also been introduced into southern Florida, USA.

Distribution on Las Islas de la Bahía: *Ctenosaura similis* is known from Guanaja and Utila.

Natural history comments: *Ctenosaura similis* is a diurnal, terrestrial to arboreal species that occurs in open areas on the Bay Islands. Adults have been seen on rocky outcrops, on fallen logs, in trees, and on buildings. Juveniles were seen in grassy fields, in pastures, in trees, on mangrove flats, on fallen logs, and on fence posts. This species is probably active throughout the year on the Bay Islands. Habitat types include hardwood forest, mangrove forest, and urban areas. *Ctenosaura similis* is known to be used as a food source by *ladinos* living on Guanaja and Utila. The recent influx of these people from the Honduran mainland has caused a decline in the populations of *C. similis* on these islands, as well as a reduction in average size.

Ctenosaura similis subadult from Isla de Guanaja. Photograph by Mikael Lundberg

Iguana iguana (Linnaeus, 1758)

Common name(s): Iguana (English and Spanish).

Description: This very large and heavy bodied lizard (males to 580 mm SVL, females to 411 mm) has a very long tail (about 2.7 to 3.2 times SVL). Raised scales can be present on the posterior portion of the head, but crests or casques are absent. The tympanum is distinct and higher than long, and a very enlarged scale is present below the tympanic region. Seven to 9 supralabials and infralabials are present to the level below the center of the eye. Many individuals have 1 or 2 raised scales on the top of the snout. Dorsal body scales are small, and most are keeled and imbricate. A distinct middorsal crest consisting of enlarged serrated scales is present; this crest is best developed in adult males. Ventral scales are small, smooth, and imbricate. Whorls with large spinous scales are absent on the tail. Caudal autotomy is absent in adults. Nine to 23 total femoral pores are present. A lateral flap of scales is absent on the hind toes. Most individuals have the dorsal surfaces of the head and body green, frequently with darker, obscure wavy crossbands on the body. Some large males can have gray dorsal surfaces. Ventral surfaces are usually pale green. The iris is usually some shade of orange or tan.

Similar species: All the members of the genus *Ctenosaura* have a tail bearing whorls of enlarged spiny scales, separated by a row or rows of intercalary scales, and no enlarged circular scale on the side of the head below the tympanum.

General geographic distribution: Low and moderate elevations on the Atlantic versant from northern Veracruz, Mexico, to southeastern Brazil and Paraguay and from southern Sinaloa, Mexico, to extreme northwestern Perú on the Pacific versant. The species also occurs in the Lesser Antilles and on numerous Caribbean islands near the mainland and several islands off the Pacific coast (see Remarks). The species is known to have been

Iguana iguana adult male from Isla de Roatán.
Photograph by Breck Bartholomew

Iguana iguana adult male from Isla de Utila. Photograph by Gunther Köhler

introduced on Hawaii and in southern Florida, USA, Puerto Rico, the Virgin Islands, and on Anguilla. Other island populations may be introduced as well.

Distribution on Las Islas de la Bahía: *Iguana iguana* is recorded from Barbareta, Guanaja, Roatán, Utila, and Cayo Cochino Pequeño.

Natural history comments: *Iguana iguana* is a diurnal, mostly arboreal (as adults) species. We have seen this lizard in trees in the interior of Roatán and on top of the brick walls of an abandoned building on Guanaja. Habitat types on the Bay Islands include hardwood forest and swamps and marshes. Local people prize the meat of this species and hunt lizards with dogs. As a result, populations of *I. iguana* on the islands are in serious decline. This species is probably active throughout the year on the Bay Islands.

Remarks: The distribution statements given in the General geographic distribution section probably includes more than one species (Malone and Davis, 2004).

Iguana iguana subadult from the Honduran mainland. Photograph by James R. McCranie

Family Polychrotidae

Polychrotids have a mental scale that is partially or completely divided by a mental groove and a male dewlap (dewlap also present in females of some species). This family of lizards includes the anoles and the genus *Polychrus* (see Frost et al., 2001; also see Schulte et al., 2003, for a conflicting hypothesis). The anoles are the only non-gekkonid lizards on the Islas de la Bahía with expanded subdigital pads. The members of this family are limited in distribution to the Western Hemisphere, where they range from the southeastern USA through Gulf coastal and Pacific coastal Mexico, thence southward through Central America to southeastern Brazil and Paraguay. They also occur on the Bahama Islands, the Greater and Lesser Antilles, Trinidad and Tobago, and on several other small Caribbean and Pacific islands near the mainland. About 330 species are presently included in this family; the number of genera is controversial. Three genera consisting of 36 species are known to occur in Honduras, of which two genera with seven species occupy the Islas de la Bahía.

Another distinctive feature of the anoles is the dewlap. All males (plus females of *Norops utilensis*) occurring on the Islas de la Bahía have brightly colored dewlaps. Males use these dewlaps for territorial displays and courtship; they extend and retract their dewlaps in a certain sequence to communicate with one another (Roughgarden, 1995). Females of *N. utilensis* were also seen to display their dewlaps while McCranie was attempting to noose them.

Anolis allisoni Barbour, 1928

Common name(s): Green Anole (English*).

Description: *Anolis allisoni* is a moderately large anole (males to about 100 mm SVL, females to about 75 mm) with a very long tail (about 1.8 to 2.2 times SVL) and an extremely long head (especially in males). The ear opening is transversely elongate with the posterior margin forming a long longitudinal depression. One scale separates the well-defined supraorbital semicircles at the narrowest point and the suboculars and supralabials are in broad contact. The anterior nasal scale is single and separated from the rostral by 1 or 2 scales and from the first supralabial by 1 scale. Postmentals number 5 or 6, with the outer pair greatly enlarged, their lengths about equal to the length of the mental scale. Lateral head scales anterior to the ear opening are slightly larger than those posterior to the ear opening. Dorsal body scales are weakly keeled, with about 3 to 5

Anolis allisoni from Isla de Roatán. Photograph by James R. McCranie

Anolis allisoni from Isla de Roatán. Photograph by Gunther Köhler

median rows slightly enlarged; the rest of the dorsals grade into the small and homogeneous laterals. Ventral scales are keeled and usually nonimbricate (a few scales can be slightly imbricate). Caudal autotomy is present. The male dewlap is large, extending posteriorly to about the level of the axillae. A dewlap is present only in males. Enlarged postcloacal scales are absent. The dorsal surface of the body is green and that of the head is turquoise blue, but these lizards quickly change to brown when stressed. The male dewlap is a deep purplish red with pale green or turquoise blue scales.

Similar species: The other anoles on the Bay Islands and Cayos Cochinos have a basically brown to gray dorsum and a vertically oval ear opening.

General geographic distribution: Low elevations of the Islas de la Bahía, Honduras, cays and islands off the coast of Belize and southern Quintana Roo, Mexico; also occurs throughout much of Cuba (exclusive of the western and eastern ends).

Distribution on Las Islas de la Bahía: *Anolis allisoni* occurs on Barbareta, Guanaja, Morat, Roatán, Cayo Cochino Grande, and Cayo Cochino Pequeño.

Natural history comments: *Anolis allisoni* is an arboreal, diurnal species that can be found on coconut palms, thorn palms, various trees, wooden fences, and buildings. The species is apparently active throughout the year. Habitat types on the Islas de la Bahía include hardwood forest, coconut groves, and urban areas.

Anolis allisoni dewlap of adult male from Isla de Guanaja. Photograph by Gunther Köhler

Norops bicaorum Köhler, 1996b

Common name(s): American Flag (English).

Description: *Norops bicaorum* is a moderately-sized anole (males to 75 mm SVL, females to 65 mm) with a very long tail (about 2.0 to 2.3 times SVL). The ear opening is vertically oval. One to 3 scales separate the well-defined supraorbital semicircles at the narrowest point and 0 or 1 scale row is present between the suboculars and supralabials. The anterior nasal scale is divided with the lower scale contacting the rostral and first supralabial. Postmentals number 6 to 8, with the outer pair not greatly enlarged, their lengths less than the length of the mental scale. Lateral head scales anterior to the ear opening are slightly larger than those posterior to the ear opening. Dorsal body scales are distinctly keeled, with about the 2 median rows slightly enlarged; the rest of the dorsals grade into the granular and homogeneous laterals. Ventral scales are strongly keeled, mucronate, and imbricate. Legs are relatively long with the shank length/SVL ratio usually more than 0.25 and the fourth toe of the adpressed hind limb reaching at least to the posterior border of the eye. Caudal autotomy is present. The male dewlap is large, extending posteriorly well beyond the level of the axillae, and the female dewlap is rudimentary. Enlarged postcloacal scales are absent. Dorsal surfaces of the head and body are some shade of brown or pale gray. Distinct dark brown lines radiate outward from the orbit and a distinct dark brown interorbital bar is present. A dark brown lyriform mark is usually present in the occipital region, but this mark can be obscure or absent altogether. The male dewlap is orange-red with a suffusion of black pigment centrally.

Similar species: *Anolis allisoni* has a green dorsum and turquoise blue head, as well as a transversely elongate ear opening. *Norops sagrei* has four postmental scales with the outer pair greatly enlarged and longer than the greatest length of the mental scale. *Norops sericeus* has a yellowish orange male dewlap with a large deep blue central spot, reaches a maximum SVL of 52 mm in males and 47 mm in females, has shorter legs (shank length/SVL usually <0.25; fourth toe of adpressed hind limb usually reaching a point between the shoulder and ear opening, occasionally between ear opening and eye), and lacks a lyriform marking on the occipital region. *Norops utilensis* has smooth ventral scales. *Norops lemuri-*

Norops bicaorum adult male from Isla de Utila. Photograph by Gunther Köhler

Norops bicaorum adult male from Isla de Utila. Photograph by Gunther Köhler

nus has a reddish orange dewlap with black and white gorgetal scales. *Norops roatanensis* has a reddish pink dewlap with a central suffusion of black pigment and a maximum SVL of 62 mm in males and 63 mm in females.

General geographic distribution: *Norops bicaorum* is endemic to Utila.

Distribution on Las Islas de la Bahía: The species occurs on the eastern portion of Utila.

Natural history comments: *Norops bicaorum* is an arboreal, diurnal species that occurs predominately on trees, including mangroves. It is extremely abundant at some localities on Utila and is probably active throughout the year. Habitat types include hardwood forest and mangrove forest.

Remarks: Specimens from Utila were included under *Anolis lemurinus* by L. Wilson and Hahn (1973).

Norops bicaorum adult female from Isla de Utila. Photograph by James R. McCranie

Norops lemurinus (Cope, 1861)

Common name(s): Ghost Anole (English; Liner, 1994).

Description: *Norops lemurinus* is a moderately-sized anole (males to 68 mm SVL, females to 79 mm) with a very long tail (about 1.7 to 2.7 times SVL). The ear opening is vertically oval. Zero to 3 scales separate the well-defined supraorbital semicircles at the narrowest point and 0 or 1 scale row is present between the suboculars and supralabials. The anterior nasal scale is divided with the lower scale contacting the rostral and first supralabial. Postmentals number 6 to 8, with the outer pair not greatly enlarged, their lengths less than the length of the mental scale. Lateral head scales anterior to the ear opening are slightly larger than those posterior to the ear opening. Dorsal body scales are distinctly keeled, with about the 2 median rows slightly enlarged; the rest of the dorsals grade into the granular and homogeneous laterals. Ventral scales are strongly keeled, mucronate, and imbricate. Legs are relatively long with the shank length/SVL ratio usually more than 0.25 and the fourth toe of the adpressed hind limb reaching at least to the posterior border of the eye. Caudal autotomy is present. The male dewlap is large, extending posteriorly slightly beyond the level of the axillae. The female dewlap is rudimentary or absent. Enlarged postcloacal scales are absent. Dorsal surfaces of the head and body are some shade of brown. Distinct dark brown lines radiate outward from the orbit and a distinct dark brown interorbital bar is present. A dark brown lyriform mark is usually present in the occipital region, but this mark can be obscure or absent altogether. The male dewlap is pinkish orange to reddish orange.

Similar species: *Anolis allisoni* has a green dorsum and turquoise blue head, as well as a transversely elongate ear opening. *Norops sagrei* has four postmental scales with the outer pair greatly enlarged and longer than the greatest length of the mental scale. *Norops sericeus* has a yellowish orange male dewlap with a large deep blue central spot, reaches a maximum SVL of 52 mm in males and 47 mm in females, and has shorter legs (shank length/SVL usually <0.25; fourth toe of adpressed hind limb usually reaching a point between the shoulder and ear opening, occasionally between ear opening and eye). *Norops utilensis* has smooth ventral scales. *Norops bicaorum* and *N. roatanensis* have pinkish red or reddish orange dewlaps with a central suffusion of black pigment. *Norops bicaorum* reaches a maximum SVL of

Norops lemurinus from the Honduran mainland. Photograph by James R. McCranie

Norops lemurinus from Cayo Cochino Pequeño. Photograph by Mikael Lundberg. Inset: Dewlap of an adult male. Photograph by Gunther Köhler

75 mm in males and 67 mm in females and *N. roatanensis* only 62 mm SVL in males and 63 mm in females.

General geographic distribution: Low and moderate elevations on the Atlantic versant from central Veracruz, Mexico, to central Panamá and disjunctly from northwestern Costa Rica to central Panamá on the Pacific versant.

Distribution on Las Islas de la Bahía: *Norops lemurinus* is recorded from Cayo Cochino Grande and Cayo Cochino Pequeño.

Natural history comments: *Norops lemurinus* a diurnal species that has been found "in shaded situations, generally on vines or small trees" in hardwood forest on the Cayos Cochinos (L. Wilson and Cruz Díaz, 1993:17).

Norops lemurinus from Cayo Cochino Pequeño. Photograph by Mikael Lundberg

Norops roatanensis Köhler and McCranie, 2001

Common name(s): American Flag (English).

Description: *Norops roatanensis* is a moderately-sized anole (males to 62 mm SVL, females to 63 mm) with a very long tail (about 2.0 to 2.3 times SVL). The ear opening is vertically oval. One to 3 scales separate the well-defined supraorbital semicircles at the narrowest point and 0 or 1 scale row is present between the suboculars and supralabials. The anterior nasal scale is divided with the lower scale contacting the rostral and first supralabial. Postmentals number 6 to 8, with the outer pair not greatly enlarged, their lengths less than the length of the mental scale. Lateral head scales anterior to the ear opening are slightly larger than those posterior to the ear opening. Dorsal body scales are distinctly keeled, with about the 2 median rows slightly enlarged; the rest of the dorsals grade into the granular and homogeneous laterals. Ventral scales are strongly keeled, mucronate, and imbricate. Legs are relatively long with the shank length/SVL ratio usually more than 0.25 and the fourth toe of the adpressed hind limb reaching at least to the posterior border of the eye. Caudal autotomy is present. The male dewlap is large, extending posteriorly slightly beyond the level of the axillae. The female dewlap is rudimentary or absent. Enlarged postcloacal scales are absent. Dorsal surfaces of the head and body are some shade of brown. Distinct dark brown lines radiate outward from the orbit and a distinct dark brown interorbital bar is present. The male dewlap is pink-red with a suffusion of black pigment centrally.

Norops roatanensis from Isla de Roatán. Photograph by Breck Bartholomew.

Similar species: *Anolis allisoni* has a green dorsum and turquoise blue head, as well as a transversely elongate ear opening. *Norops sagrei* has four postmental scales with the outer pair greatly enlarged and longer than the greatest length of the mental scale. *Norops sericeus* has a yellowish orange male dewlap with a large deep blue central spot, reaches a maximum SVL of 52 mm in males and 47 mm in females, and has shorter legs (shank length/SVL usually <0.25; fourth toe of adpressed hind limb usually reaching a point between the shoulder and ear opening, occasionally between ear opening and eye). *Norops utilensis* has smooth ventral scales. *Norops lemurinus* has a reddish orange dewlap with black and white gorgetal scales and reaches maximum SVL of 68 mm in males and 77 mm in females. *Norops bicaorum* has a reddish orange dewlap with a central suffusion of black pigment and reaches a maximum SVL of 75 mm in males and 67 mm in females.

Norops roatanensis from Isla de Roatán.
Photograph by Gunther Köhler

General geographic distribution: *Norops roatanensis* is endemic to Roatán.

Distribution on Las Islas de la Bahía: See General geographic distribution.

Natural history comments: *Norops roatanensis* is a diurnal, primarily arboreal species that occurs on various tree trunks in hardwood forest. The species can also be found on the ground, but they attempt to escape by running to the nearest tree and climbing the trunk. This species is probably active throughout the year.

Remarks: Specimens from Roatán were referred to *Anolis lemurinus* by L. Wilson and Hahn (1973).

Norops roatanensis from Isla de Roatán.
Photograph by James R. McCranie.

Norops sagrei (Duméril and Bibron, 1837)

Common name(s): Brown Anole (English; Liner, 1994).

Description: *Norops sagrei* is a moderately-sized anole (males to 70 mm SVL, females to 57 mm [Lee, 1996]) with a long tail (about 1.4 to 2.0 times SVL). The ear opening is vertically oval. One scale separates the well-defined supraorbital semicircles at the narrowest point and the suboculars are in broad contact with the supralabials. The anterior nasal scale is single and contacts the rostral, but usually not the first supralabial. Postmentals number 4, with the outer pair greatly enlarged, their lengths greater than the length of the mental scale. Lateral head scales anterior to the ear opening are distinctly larger than those posterior to the ear opening. Dorsal body scales are keeled, with 8 or 9 median rows slightly enlarged; the rest of the dorsals grade into the granular and homogeneous laterals. Ventral scales are distinctly keeled and imbricate. Caudal autotomy is present. The male dewlap is moderately large, extending posteriorly to a level anterior to the axillae. The female dewlap is rudimentary. Enlarged postcloacal scales are present in males. Dorsal surfaces of the head and body are some shade of brown, with darker brown spots, bars, or chevrons. Females can have a pale brown, broad middorsal stripe. The male dewlap is dark orange with gray or brown stippled white scales.

Similar species: *Anolis allisoni* has a green dorsum and turquoise blue head, as well as a transversely elongate ear opening. All the other Bay Island and Cayos Cochinos anoles have five or more postmental scales, with the outer pair not greatly enlarged and much shorter than the greatest length of the mental scale.

General geographic distribution: Low elevations of Cuba, the Bahama Islands, Jamaica, the Cayman Islands, the Swan Islands, Roatán Island, and many islands off the coast of Belize and Quintana Roo, Mexico. It also occurs along the coast on the mainland of Middle America from western Campeche, Mexico, to north-central Honduras, as well

Norops sagrei from Isla de Roatán.
Photograph by James R. McCranie.

Norops sagrei from Isla de Roatán.
Photograph by James R. McCranie

as in the central portion of the Yucatán Peninsula. Many of these populations are likely introduced by man. This human commensal species is also widely introduced in Hawaii and peninsula Florida, USA, and other localities in the southeastern USA. It is also known to be introduced on Grenada in the Lesser Antilles.

Distribution on Las Islas de la Bahía: *Norops sagrei* is recorded only from Roatán.

Natural history comments: *Norops sagrei* is a diurnal, primarily arboreal species that is found on buildings, fences, palm trunks, and mangrove trees in urban areas near the coast. The populations on the Bay Islands may have been introduced by man. The species is probably active throughout the year.

Remarks: This species was includ-ed under *Anolis sagrei* by L. Wilson and Hahn (1973).

Norops sagrei as illustrated in Sagra (1839–1843).

Norops sericeus (Hallowell, "1856" [1857])

Common name(s): Silky Anole (English; Liner, 1994).

Description: *Norops sericeus* is a small anole (males to 52 mm SVL, females to 47 mm [Savage, 2002]) with a very long tail (about 1.8 to 2.3 times SVL). The ear opening is more or less oval. Zero to 2 (usually 1) scales separate the well-defined supraorbital semicircles at the narrowest point and the suboculars are in broad contact with the supralabials. The anterior nasal scale is single or divided, with the lower edge, or the lower scale, contacting the rostral. Postmentals number 5 to 7, with the outer pair not greatly enlarged, their lengths not greater than the length of the mental. Lateral head scales anterior to the ear opening are slightly larger than those posterior to the ear opening. Dorsal body scales are keeled, with 6 to 8 median rows slightly enlarged; the rest of the dorsals grade into the granular and homogeneous laterals. Ventral scales are keeled and imbricate. Legs are relatively short with the shank length/SVL ratio usually less than 0.25 and the fourth toe of the adpressed hind limb usually reaching to a point between the shoulder and ear opening (occasionally reaching between the ear opening and the eye). Caudal autotomy is present. The male dewlap is large, extending posteriorly slightly past the level of the axillae. The female dewlap is rudimentary. Enlarged postcloacal scales are absent. Dorsal surfaces of the head and body are gray to bronze with a silky sheen. A few indistinct darker brown spots or reticulations can be present on the body. The male dewlap is yellowish orange with a blue or purple central spot.

Similar species: *Anolis allisoni* has a green dorsum and turquoise blue head, as well as a transversely elongate ear opening. *Norops sagrei* has four postmental scales with the outer pair greatly enlarged and longer than the greatest length of the mental scale. *Norops utilensis* has smooth ventral scales. *Norops bicaorum, N. lemurinus,* and *N. roatanensis* have a pinkish red, red, or reddish orange dewlap, with or without a central suffusion of black pigment and longer legs (shank length/SVL >0.25; fourth toe of adpressed hind limb reaching at least to

Norops sericeus from the Honduran mainland. Photograph by James R. McCranie

Norops sericeus from Isla de Utila. Photograph by Breck Bartholomew

posterior border of eye). These three species are also larger (SVL to more than 60 mm in both sexes) than *N. sericeus*.

General geographic distribution: Low and moderate elevations of the Atlantic versant from central Tamaulipas, Mexico, to northeastern Nicaragua. It also occurs on the Atlantic versant in southern Nicaragua, extreme northern Costa Rica, and southeastern Costa Rica. Occurs on the Pacific versant from eastern Oaxaca, Mexico, to west-central Costa Rica. It is also found on Isla del Maíz Grande, Nicaragua, and Isla Mujeres, Quintana Roo, Mexico.

Distribution on Las Islas de la Bahía: *Norops sericeus* is known only from Utila.

Natural history comments: *Norops sericeus* is a diurnal species that is usually found in bushes and on fence posts in open areas in hardwood forest. It can also be found on the ground in open areas. The species is probably active throughout the year on Utila.

Remarks: This species was included under the name *Anolis sericeus* by L. Wilson and Hahn (1973).

Norops sericeus dewlap from Isla de Utila. Photograph by Gunther Köhler

Norops utilensis Köhler, 1996a

Common name(s): Mangrove Anole (English*).

Description: *Norops utilensis* is a moderately-sized anole (males to 59 mm SVL, females to
58 mm) with a long tail (about 1.5 to 1.6 times
SVL). The ear opening is vertically oval. The well-
defined supraorbital semicircles are in contact medially, as are the suboculars and supralabials. The
anterior nasal is divided and separated from the rostral by 1 scale. Postmentals number 5 to 7, with the
outermost pair not greatly enlarged, their lengths
less than the length of the mental scale. Lateral head
scales anterior to the ear opening are slightly larger

than those posterior to the ear opening. Dorsal body scales are small, most are smooth, and
the small lateral scales are heterogeneous. Ventral scales are smooth and slightly conical.
Caudal autotomy is present. The male dewlap is moderately large, extending posteriorly
slightly beyond the level of the axillae. The female dewlap is well developed and is only
slightly smaller than the male dewlap. Enlarged postcloacal scales are absent. Dorsal surfaces
of the head and body have a lichenose pattern and a color repertory from some shade of
brown to white or pale gray. Both the male and female dewlaps are red.

Similar species: *Anolis allisoni* has a green dorsum and turquoise blue head, as well
as a transversely elongate ear opening. All other species of *Norops* on the Bay Islands and
Cayos Cochinos have distinctly keeled ventral scales.

General geographic distribution: *Norops utilensis* is endemic to Utila.

Distribution on Las Islas de la Bahía: The species is known only from the eastern
end of Isla de Utila.

Natural history comments: *Norops utilensis* is a diurnal species that is known only
from two areas of mangrove forest on Utila. The species is apparently absent from other
seemingly similar mangrove forests on the island. It is infrequently observed and is usually
found high in trees. Gutsche et al. (2004) provided some natural history observations on this
species, including aggregate nesting behavior.

Norops utilensis from Isla de Utila.
Photograph by James R. McCranie.
Dewlap photograph above by Gunther
Köhler

Norops utilensis from Isla de Utila.
Photograph by Gunther Köhler

Norops utilensis from Isla de Utila.
Photograph by Joe Burgess

Norops utilensis from Isla de Utila.
Photograph by Joe Burgess

Family Scincidae

Skinks are exceedingly variable, but most are characterized by smooth, shiny cycloid scales underlain by osteoderms comprised of a mosaic of smaller bones, giving the body a very hard exterior (Pough et al., 2003). The members of this family of lizards are found nearly worldwide. In the Western Hemisphere, they occur from southern British Columbia, Canada, and most of the USA southward through Mexico and Central America to western Ecuador west of the Andes and to north-central Argentina east of the Andes. Members also occur on Trinidad and Tobago, Jamaica, Hispaniola, Puerto Rico and nearby islands, the Virgin Islands, the Turks and Caicos Islands, and the Lesser Antilles. They range throughout the Eastern Hemisphere south of about 42°N to the southern tips of Africa, Australia, and New Zealand. About 115 genera comprising 1260 species were included in this family by Pough et al. (2003). Four genera with six included species are known to occupy Honduras. Two species from two genera occur on the Islas de la Bahía.

Mabuya unimarginata Cope, 1862b

Common name(s): Shiny Skink (English*).

Description: This medium-sized lizard (56 to 91 mm SVL [Savage, 2002]) has a long tail (about 1.4 times SVL). The narrow head is barely distinct from the attenuate body and has enlarged, symmetrical scales dorsally. The snout is pointed when viewed dorsally, and the lower eyelid possesses a translucent disk. Two supranasal (internasal) and 2 frontoparietal scales are present. Dorsal, lateral, and ventral scales are smooth, cycloid, and imbricate, and are uniform in size. The slender tail is round in cross-section, with smooth, cycloid, and imbricate scales on the dorsal, lateral, and subcaudal surfaces. Five digits are present on the forelimbs. Femoral pores are absent. This shiny lizard has a metallic appearance, with gray

Mabuya unimarginata from Isla de Utila. Photograph by Robert Powell

Mabuya unimarginata from Isla de Utila. Photograph by Gunther Köhler

to brown dorsal surfaces and a broad, deep brown or black lateral stripe extending from the snout, across the eye and tympanum, to the area of the hind limb. Below the dark stripe is a pale gray, cream, or iridescent green stripe extending from the tip of the snout to the groin area. Ventral surfaces are a patternless gray, tan, cream, or pale green. The iris is black.

Similar species: *Sphenomorphus cherriei* lacks supranasal scales and has a single frontoparietal scale. *Gymnophthalmus speciosus* lacks moveable eyelids and has only four digits on the forelimbs.

General geographic distribution: Low, moderate, and rarely intermediate elevations on the Atlantic versant from northeastern Hidalgo, Mexico, to Panamá and from southern Jalisco, Mexico, to Panamá on the Pacific versant. In addition to the Bay Islands, the species also occurs on islands off the coast of Belize and Quintana Roo, Mexico, and several islands off the Pacific coast.

Distribution on Las Islas de la Bahía: *Mabuya unimarginata* is recorded from Guanaja, Roatán, and Utila.

Natural history comments: This diurnal species was said to be largely arboreal on Utila by L. Wilson and Hahn (1973), who recorded one from 8 m up the trunk of a mango tree. An individual was seen on Guanaja in a hole in a dead, standing coconut palm trunk. The species occurs in hardwood forest and coconut groves on the Bay Islands.

Remarks: L. Wilson and Hahn (1973) used the combination *Mabuya mabouya* for this species.

Sphenomorphus cherriei (Cope, 1893)

Common name(s): Brown Skink (English*).

Description: This small lizard (males to 58 mm SVL, females to 68 mm [Savage, 2002]) has a long tail (about 1.4 to 1.5 times SVL). The short, broad head is slightly distinct from the body, and has enlarged symmetrical scales dorsally. The snout is short and rounded when viewed dorsally, and the lower eyelid usually lacks a translucent disk. One frontoparietal plate is present. Supranasal (internasal) scales are absent and a single frontoparietal scale is present. Dorsal, lateral, and ventral scales are smooth, cycloid, and imbricate, and all are about the same size. The slender tail is round in cross-section, with smooth, cycloid, and imbricate scales on the dorsal, lateral, and subcaudal surfaces. Five digits are present on the forelimbs. Femoral pores are absent. Dorsal color is brown and the lateral surfaces are usually a paler shade of brown. The upper lip is spotted with dark brown. A black lateral stripe extends posteriorly from the tip of the snout, across the eye and tympanum, onto the body where it breaks up into smaller black dots or disappears altogether. This stripe is bordered ventrally by a narrow white or yellow stripe that also diffuses posteriorly. Ventral surfaces are uniformly gray, tan, or cream. The iris is black.

Similar species: *Mabuya unimarginata* has paired supranasal (internasal) and fron-

Sphenomorphus cherriei from Honduran mainland. Photograph by Mikael Lundberg

Sphenomorphus cherriei from Cayo Cochino Pequeño. Photograph by Mikael Lundberg

toparietal scales. *Gymnophthalmus speciosus* lacks moveable eyelids and has only four digits on the forelimbs.

General geographic distribution: Low, moderate, and occasionally intermediate elevations on the Atlantic versant from central Veracruz, Mexico, to extreme western Panamá and from northwestern Costa Rica to extreme western Panamá on the Pacific versant. Apparently isolated populations also occur on the outer end and central portion of the Yucatán Peninsula, Mexico; also occurs on Isla del Maíz Grande, Nicaragua, in addition to Cayo Cochino Pequeño.

Distribution on Las Islas de la Bahía: *Sphenomorphus cherriei* is known only from Cayo Cochino Pequeño.

Natural history comments: This diurnal species can be found in leaf litter in hardwood forest. It can be extremely common at some localities on mainland Honduras, but appears to be uncommon on Cayo Cochino Pequeño.

Remarks: Lundberg (2002) recently reported this species from Cayo Cochino Pequeño, the first record for Las Islas de la Bahía.

Sphenomorphus cherriei from Cayo Cochino Pequeño. Photograph by Mikael Lundberg

Family Gymnophthalmidae

The combination of having infralingual plicae and the lack of eyelids will distinguish the Honduran member of this family from all other lizard families on the Bay Islands. This family is restricted in distribution to the Neotropics, where it occurs from southern Chiapas, Mexico, and Belize southward to northwestern Perú west of the Andes and central Argentina east of the Andes. It also occurs on Trinidad and Tobago and the Lesser Antilles (some of the Lesser Antilles populations are introduced). Thirty-seven genera consisting of 178 species were included in this family by Pellegrino et al. (2001), but the taxonomy of these lizards is unsettled. One species is presently known to occur in Honduras, including the Bay Islands.

Gymnophthalmus speciosus (Hallowell, "1860" [1861])

Common name(s): Redtail Ground Lizard (English*).

Description: This small lizard attains a maximum known SVL of 42 mm in males and 44 mm in females. The tail is long (about 1.7 to 2.0 times SVL). The dorsal surface of the head is covered with large plates. Moveable eyelids are absent. Gular scales are cycloid in shape. Five to 7 supralabials and 6 to 8 infralabials are present. Dorsal and ventral body scales are smooth and cycloid in shape. Limbs are short and small, and only 4 digits are present on the forelimbs. Four to 13 total femoral pores are present in males; femoral pores are absent in females. The dorsum is some shade of brown, usually with a metallic sheen. A pale brown or white line is usually present along the upper border of the dark brown lateral surfaces. The tail is bright red in juveniles and reddish orange in adults, if not regenerated. The belly varies from white in many subadults to heavily suffused with black in adult males.

Similar species: *Mabuya unimarginata* and *Sphenomorphus cherriei* have moveable eyelids and five digits on the forelimbs.

Gymnophthalmus speciosus from Isla de Guanaja. Photograph by Gunther Köhler

Gymnophthalmus speciosus from Isla de Roatán. Photograph by James R. McCranie

General geographic distribution: Low and moderate elevations on the Atlantic versant from northern Belize to Guyana and from eastern Oaxaca, Mexico, to Panamá on the Pacific versant (see Remarks). The species also occurs on the islands of Trinidad and Tobago.

Distribution on Las Islas de la Bahía: *Gymnophthalmus speciosus* is known from Barbareta, Guanaja, and Roatán.

Natural history comments: *Gymnophthalmus speciosus* is a terrestrial or semi-fossorial, diurnal species. It is usually active in leaf litter and can be found by raking through fallen leaves and other ground debris in hardwood forest and coconut groves.

Remarks: The range given in the General geographic distribution section probably encompasses ranges of more than one species (Kizirian and Cole, 1999).

Gymnophthalmus speciosus from Isla de Roatán. Photograph by James R. McCranie

Family Teiidae

The combination of having infralingual plicae and moveable eyelids will distinguish the teiids from all other lizards in the area. The members of this family are restricted in distribution to the Western Hemisphere, where they are found from Maryland westward to Idaho and Oregon, USA, southward through Mexico and Central America to central Chile west of the Andes and central Argentina east of the Andes. Members also occur on the Bahama Islands, the Greater and Lesser Antilles, and Trinidad and Tobago. Nine genera comprised of 125 species were included in this family by Pough et al. (2003). Also, Reeder et al. (2002) presented evidence rejecting the monophyly of the genus *Cnemidophorus*. Three genera containing six species are currently known to occupy Honduras, with one species occurring on the Islas de la Bahía.

Cnemidophorus lemniscatus (Linnaeus, 1758)

Common name(s): Shake-paw (English).

Description: This moderately-sized lizard attains a maximum known SVL of 113 mm in males and 93 mm in females (Savage, 2002). The tail is very long (about 1.9 to 2.6 times SVL). The dorsal surface of the head is covered with large plates. Moveable eyelids are present. Four parietal scales and 1 interparietal scale are present. The anterior gular scales are much larger than those that are more posterior; the central gular scales are not greatly enlarged. Three or 4 regular transverse rows of enlarged mesoptychial scales are present. Supralabials number 6 to 9 and infralabials 5 to 9. Dorsal body scales are granular and smooth. Ventral scales are large, platelike, and smooth, and are in 8 to 10 (usually 8) transverse rows. Two or 3 rows of enlarged scales occur on the dorsolateral surfaces of the upper arms. Limbs

Cnemidophorus lemniscatus adult male from Isla de Utila. Photograph by Joe Burgess

Cnemidophorus lemniscatus adult female from Isla de Roatán. Photograph by Breck Bartholomew

are large and have 5 digits each. Total femoral pores number 30 to 66. A precloacal spur is present on each side of the precloacal plate in males. Juveniles and adult females have dorsal and lateral ground colors of brown or black, or these colors are suffused with green, and have 7 to 10 pale longitudinal stripes. Adult males have a middorsal body ground color of brown and the flanks are pinkish tan, rust-red, or yellowish brown (or various colors in between). About 3 rows of yellow to white spots occur on the lateral surfaces and usually no more than 4 pale stripes on the dorsal and dorsolateral areas in adult males. The belly is some shade of green in males and white in juveniles and adult females; a bluish tinge to the belly color can be present in both sexes.

Similar species: No other lizard on the Bay Islands and Cayos Cochinos has granular dorsal and lateral scales and large, smooth, quadrangular ventral scales.

General geographic distribution: Low elevations of the Atlantic versant from southern Belize to eastern Honduras, and from eastern Panamá to northern Brazil; also on the Pacific versant in central and eastern Panamá. The species occurs on several Caribbean islands, including Trinidad and Tobago, in addition to the Bay Islands (see Remarks).

Distribution on Las Islas de la Bahía: *Cnemidophorus lemniscatus* occurs on Roatán, Utila, and Cayo Cochino Pequeño.

Natural history comments: *Cnemidophorus lemniscatus* is a terrestrial, diurnal, quickly moving heliothermic species that occurs in sandy areas above the high-tide mark (beach areas and associated vegetation and coconut groves) on the Islas de la Bahía. The peculiar habit of pausing to lift and shake one of the forelegs as its moves over the sand is the origin of the English common name for the species. *Cnemidophorus lemniscatus* is probably active on sunny days throughout the year on the Islas de la Bahía.

Remarks: The range given in the General geographic distribution section probably represents the ranges of more than one species (Reeder et al., 2002). Barbour (1928) described the subspecies *Cnemidophorus lemniscatus ruatanus* based on one specimen from Roatán. Presently, *C. l. ruatanus* is considered a synonym of *C. l. lemniscatus*. However, the Bay Island specimens differ from the mainland Honduran specimens in several characters (see L. Wilson and Hahn, 1973). Given that *C. lemniscatus* probably represents more than one species (Reeder et al., 2002), the systematic status of the Bay Island populations currently assigned to *C. lemniscatus* remains unresolved.

Cnemidophorus lemniscatus adult male from Isla de Roatán. Photograph by Breck Bartholomew

Snakes

The known snake fauna of Honduras consists of 120 species (McCranie, 2004; McCranie and Castañeda, 2004; McCranie et al., 2003b; L. Wilson and McCranie, 2002; L. Wilson et al., 2003), of which 19 occur on the Bay Islands and Cayos Cochinos. Features that will distinguish snakes from lizards are discussed in the section on the latter reptiles. Snakes on the Islas de la Bahía range in size from the tiny *Leptotyphlops goudotii* to the large *Boa constrictor*. Drawings illustrating some of the snake scales mentioned in various species descriptions are included in Figs. 35–37.

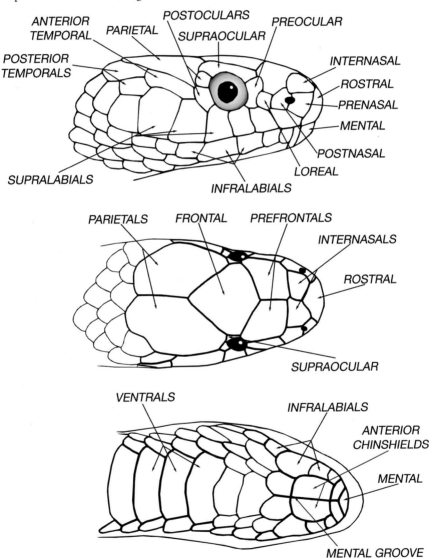

Figure 35. Pertinent scales of the head of a colubrid snake. Modified from Fig. 403 in Köhler (2003).

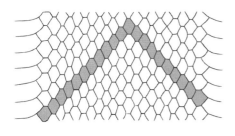

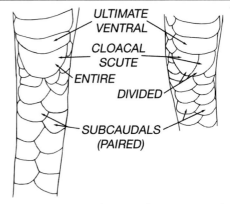

Figure 36. Method of counting dorsal scale rows in snakes (shaded). The example has 21 scale rows. Modified from Fig. 436 in Köhler (2003).

Figure 37. Ventral view of posterior end of body and anterior section of tail of a colubrid snake. Modified from Fig. 437 in Köhler (2003)

Key to the Species of Snakes of the Bay Islands and Cayos Cochinos

1   A. Ventral scales not enlarged, same size and shape as the dorsal scales
....*Leptotyphlops goudotii* (p. 127)
    B. Ventral scales enlarged, much wider than scales of the dorsum.............................. 2
2   A. Ventral scales not extending the full width of the body; dorsal scales in 55 to 95 rows at midbody; a pair of cloacal spurs present on either side of the vent
....*Boa constrictor* (p. 129)
    B. Ventral scales extending the entire width of the body; dorsal scale rows fewer than 35 at midbody; cloacal spurs absent 3
3   A. A pair of rigid, hollow fangs present on the anterior portions of the maxillary bones; dorsal pattern of red and black rings................................ *Micrurus ruatanus* (p. 162)
    B. No pair of rigid, hollow fangs present on the anterior portions of the maxillary bones, although grooved fangs may be situated on posterior portions of the maxillary bone; dorsal pattern not consisting of red and black rings.. 4
4   A. Body and tail extremely attenuate; head blunt and very distinctly set off from slender neck ....*Imantodes cenchoa* (p. 145)
    B. Shape of head, body, and tail not as above 5
5   A. Cloacal scute entire; a diagonal black mark present on neck
....*Drymarchon melanurus* (p. 138)
    B. Cloacal scute divided; diagonal black mark absent on neck................................... 6
6   A. Dorsal scales in 15 or 17 rows at midbody... 7
    B. Dorsal scales in 19 or more rows at midbody... 15
7   A. Dorsal scales in 11 rows anterior to vent..................... *Leptophis mexicanus* (p. 148)
    B. Dorsal scales in 13, 15, or 17 rows anterior to vent... 8
8   A. Dorsal scales in 13 rows anterior to vent... 9
    B. Dorsal scales in 15 or 17 rows anterior to vent.. 11

9   A. Supralabials usually 8 or 9; dorsum pale brown to gray; no ventrolateral longitudinal pale stripes .... *Oxybelis aeneus* (p. 150)

    B. Supralabials usually 10; dorsum green or mustard yellow; venter with two longitudinal white or pale yellow stripes near lateral edges **10**

10 A. Dorsum uniformly green in life .... *Oxybelis fulgidus* (p. 152)

    B. Dorsum uniformly mustard yellow in life .... *Oxybelis wilsoni* (p. 154)

11 A. Dorsum of body with three pale stripes on a darker ground color .... *Tantilla tritaeniata* (p. 158)

    B. Dorsal body color not as above **12**

12 A. Two scales between postnasal scale and eye .... *Dryadophis melanolomus* (p. 136)

    B. One scale between postnasal scale and eye **13**

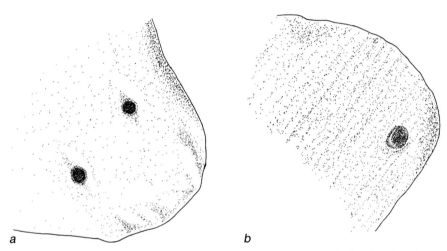

Figure 38. Paired (a) and single (b) apical pits on the posterior end of a dorsal scale in a colubrid snake. Drawings by Philipp Groß.

13 A. Paired apical pits present on most dorsal scales (Fig. 38) .... *Enulius bifoveatus* (p. 140)

    B. Single apical pit present on most dorsal scales (Fig. 38) **14**

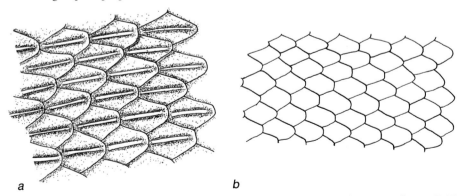

Figure 39. Snake dorsal scales showing: (a) keeled condition (*Tretanorhinus nigroluteus*; SMF 77096); (b) smooth condition (*Coniophanes imperialis*; SMF 77095). Drawings by Philipp Groß.

14 A. Pale nuchal collar absent...*Enulius roatanensis* (p. 144)
   B. Pale nuchal collar present...*Enulius flavitorques* (p. 142)
15 A. Dorsal scales in 27 to 34 rows at midbody; more than 240 ventral scales
   ....*Pseudelaphe flavirufa* (p. 156)
   B. Dorsal scales in 19 to 23 rows at midbody; fewer than 215 ventral scales............ 16
16 A. Dorsal scales keeled (Fig. 39) .... *Tretanorhinus nigroluteus* (p. 160)
   B. Dorsal scales smooth (Fig. 39) 17
17 A. Dorsal pattern consisting of spots or blotches; pupil vertically elliptical
   ....*Leptodeira septentrionalis* (p. 146)
   B. Dorsal pattern consisting of stripes; pupil circular 18
18 A. Dorsal scales in 19 rows at midbody; venter usually immaculate, but small dark spots
   can be present on anterior edges of ventral scales
   .... *Coniophanes imperialis* (p. 134)
   B. Dorsal scales in 21 rows at midbody; venter with double row of large, regular dark
   spots, one pair to a ventral scale ....*Coniophanes bipunctatus* (p. 132)

Family Leptotyphlopidae

The Islas de la Bahía representative of this family is the only snake in the area to have small ventral scales that are the same size as the dorsal scales. This family ranges in the Western Hemisphere from the southwestern USA southward through Mexico and Central America and into South America (except for the high Andes) as far south as southern coastal Perú, and central Argentina, as well as the Caribbean region (Bahamas, Hispaniola, and the Lesser Antilles). In the Eastern Hemisphere, it ranges in western Asia from Turkey to northwestern India and on the continent of Africa, as well as on Socotra Island. Two genera comprising 87 species were included in this family by McDiarmid et al. (1999) and two genera with approximately 90 species by Pough et al. (2003). One species is known to occupy Honduras, including the Islas de la Bahía.

Leptotyphlops goudotii from Isla de Guanaja.
Photograph by Gunther Köhler.

Leptotyphlops goudotii (Duméril and Bibron, 1844)

Common name(s): Silver Snake (English).

Description: This small (to about 185 mm in total length [TL]), slender, elongate blind snake has a rounded head of the same diameter as the cylindrical body, smooth, rounded, close-fitting dorsal and ventral scales of the same size in 14 rows, and a short, blunt tail terminating in a spine. Eyes are vestigial, and located beneath enlarged ocular scales. Middorsal scales from rostral scale to tail spine number from 220 to 244. Subcaudal scales range from 15 to 20. The color pattern consists of small dark spots arranged in longitudinal lines coursing down the middle of each longitudinal scale row. A pale, often yellow spot is present each on the snout and the tip of the tail.

Similar species: No other species of snake can be confused with this tiny worm snake. All other snakes in the region have enlarged ventral scales that are much wider than those of the dorsum and have the eye surrounded by an ocular groove, instead of placed beneath an ocular scale.

General geographic distribution: Low, moderate, and occasionally intermediate elevations from Veracruz, Mexico, on the Atlantic versant and Colima, Mexico, on the Pacific versant through Central America to Venezuela and Colombia. In addition to the Bay Islands, it also occurs on the following islands: Cozumel, the Swan Islands of Honduras, San Andrés, Providencia, Bonaire, the Suma Islands, Margarita, and Trinidad.

Distribution on Las Islas de la Bahía: *Leptotyphlops goudotii* is recorded from Barbareta, Guanaja, Roatán, Utila, Cayo Cochino Grande, and Cayo Cochino Pequeño.

Natural history comments: *Leptotyphlops goudotii* is a fossorial species that has been found inside termite nests, under rocks and leaves on the forest floor, under debris on the floor of an abandoned stilt house, under debris around a leaf-cutter ant nest, under a rock in a dry stream bed, under a rock on a beach, and crawling on a rocky outcrop during the day on the Islas de la Bahía. The species is apparently both diurnal and nocturnal. Habitat types on the Bay Islands and Cayos Cochinos include hardwood forest and ironshore formations.

Leptotyphlops goudotii from Isla de Guanaja.
Photograph by Mikael Lundberg

Leptotyphlops goudotii (showing yellow tail-tip) from
Isla de Guanaja. Photograph by Gunther Köhler

Remarks: Taylor (1940) described a specimen of this species from Utila as a distinct species *Leptotyphlops magnamaculata*. L. Wilson and Hahn (1973), under the name *L. phenops*, discussed a few differences between the Bay Island and mainland populations, but decided that the Bay Island populations were conspecific with those from the mainland. As reported by L. Wilson and Hahn (1973), these tiny snakes, if eaten by chickens, are said to be able to make their way completely along the bird's digestive tract and exit via the cloaca. Given the burrowing capability of these snakes, perhaps this claim is not a myth, although we doubt that these snakes possess such a capacity.

Family Boidae

The family Boidae includes the snakes typically referred to as boas, sand boas, and pythons. The largest snakes in the world belong to this family, but some boas are rather small. The boas have many small scales on the dorsum of the head, retain externally visible remnants of posterior limbs, give birth to living young (viviparous), and constrict their prey. Some boas have infrared-sensitive labial pits. The members of this family are found in the Western Hemisphere from southern British Columbia and extreme southwestern Alberta, Canada, and from central Tamaulipas, Mexico, southward (including Baja California) through Central America and into South America to about latitude 35°S, as well as in the West Indies. In the Eastern Hemisphere, they occur from southeastern Europe to Asia Minor, and southward into northern, central, and eastern Africa, Madagascar, and Reunion Island, and eastward through the Arabian Peninsula, central and southwestern Asia to India and Sri Lanka, as well as the Moluccas and New Guinea through Melanesia to Samoa. Ten genera (McDiarmid et al., 1999; Austin, 2000) containing 41 species (McDiarmid et al., 1999) were included in this family in the most recent summaries. Two genera comprising two species are currently known to occupy Honduras, with one species occupying the Islas de la Bahía.

Boa constrictor from Cayo Cochino Pequeño.
Photograph by Mikael Lundberg

Boa constrictor Linnaeus, 1758

Common name(s): Boa (English and Spanish); Waula (corrupted English).

Description: The common boa is a large terrestrial to arboreal snake (to about 5500 mm TL, but individuals found in nature are usually much smaller) with no enlarged plates on the dorsum of the head or any labial pits. It possesses 64 to 79 (55 to 95) dorsal scale rows at midbody and 19 to 22 (17 to 25) supralabials. Ventral scales are relatively narrow and do not reach the lateral edges of the venter; they number 229 to 251 (223 to 288). Subcaudals number 51 to 64 (43 to 70). A pair of horny spurs is present on either side of the vent in both males and females, but is better developed in males. The pupil is vertically elliptical. The head is well set off from the neck, as a consequence of the massive jaw musculature. The dorsum of the length of the body is gray to tan with a series of anteriorly H-shaped dark brown dorsal blotches. The top of the head is the same ground color as that of the body, often with a dark brown median line extending from the snout to the nape. The venter is pale gray to tan with dark lateral blotches.

Similar species: No other species of snake is likely to be confused with this well-known species. All other snakes in the area, save for *Leptotyphlops goudotii*, have the ventral scales extending the full width of the venter and have a set of enlarged plates on the top of the head. *Leptotyphlops goudotii* is a blind snake, is tiny in size, has dorsal and ventral scales the same size and shape, and has the eyes located beneath ocular scales.

General geographic distribution: Low and moderate elevations from central Tamaulipas, Mexico, on the Atlantic versant and northern Sonora, Mexico, on the Pacific versant through Central America to central Argentina and Uruguay east of the Andes and north-western Perú west of the Andes. The species also occurs on numerous islands along both coasts.

Distribution on Las Islas de la Bahía: *Boa constrictor* is known from Barbareta, Guanaja, Roatán, Utila, Cayo Cochino Grande, and Cayo Cochino Pequeño.

Natural history comments: We found individuals of *Boa constrictor* on the Bay Islands crossing roads at night, under trash at a dump, and coiled by day in trees in a mangrove swamp. Emmons and Werfel (*in* Bermingham et al., 1998:33), in discussing mammals on the Cayos Cochinos, stated, "An interesting local rumour holds that agoutis [*Dasyprocta* cf. *punctata*] only became numerous when permits were given to collect boas on the island [Cayo Cochino Grande] for the pet trade, and 5,000 boas were taken within two years." Habitat types on the Islas de la Bahía include hardwood forest and mangrove forest.

Remarks: The pet trade animals mentioned above were frequently offered for sale in the 1980s under the name Hog (or Hogg) Island Boas. Captive offspring from this stock are still occasionally offered for sale. In addition, illegal trafficking in wild caught boas from the Cayos Cochinos continues. Two men with 25 recently caught Cayos Cochinos boas were arrested in the mainland port city of La Ceiba in January 2004 (Miami Herald, 23 January 2004). McCranie also saw (November 1989) an adult on Roatán that was being skinned "for a belt." Price and Russo (1991) suggested that the Boa from the Bay Islands and Cayos Cochinos represents an undescribed species. However, as indicated by L. Wilson and Meyer (1985), a range-wide systematic review of *Boa constrictor* is needed before new names are proposed for various populations of this widespread taxon.

Boa constrictor from Cayo Cochino Grande.
Photograph by Mikael Lundberg

Boa constrictor from Isla de Utila. Photograph by Gunther Köhler.
Inset: from Cayos Cochinos. Photograph by Mikael Lundberg

Boa constrictor from Isla de Utila. Photograph by Breck Bartholomew

Family Colubridae

The family Colubridae has no known synapomorphies and may be paraphyletic (Pough et al., 2003). Characterization of the family as presently envisioned is, thus, difficult or impossible to provide. This family of snakes, the largest of "approximately 15 families" recognized (Pough et al., 2003:147), is distributed in the Western Hemisphere from Canada throughout the USA, Mexico, Central America, South America, and the West Indies. In the Eastern Hemisphere, colubrids are found throughout Europe, Africa, Asia, Australia, and some islands of Oceania. Approximately 320 genera with more than 1800 species are included in this family (Pough et al., 2003). Fifty genera comprising 97 species are known to occur in Honduras. Eleven genera containing 16 species occur on the Islas de la Bahía.

Coniophanes bipunctatus (Günther, 1858)

Common name(s): Nightwalker (English).

Description: This snake is medium-sized (to about 750 mm TL), with a moderately long tail. The head is distinct from the neck. The pupil is circular and 2 scales (a loreal and a preocular) are between the postnasal and eye. Supralabials number 7 to 9, usually 8, with the fourth and fifth bordering the orbit. Infralabials number 7 to 11, usually 9 or 10. Ventrals range from 124 to 137 (124 to 145) and subcaudals from 78 to 96 (72 to 101). The cloacal scute is divided. Dorsal scales are smooth, without apical pits, in 21(23)–21–17(19) rows. Dorsal ground color is pale brown through dark brown to reddish brown, with a dark brown lateral stripe present usually only on rows 4 and 5, sometimes only on row 3, and a diffuse, dark brown stripe extending the length of the middorsal scale row. Venter is cream to yellow anteriorly, grading to pinkish orange posteriorly, or cream medially and pinkish orange laterally, with conspicuous dark brown to black rounded spots, usually one pair to each ventral scale, decreasing in size posteriorly. Supralabials, chin, and throat are mottled or lined with white and brown pigment.

Coniophanes bipunctatus from Isla de Roatán.
Photograph by Breck Bartholomew.

Coniophanes bipunctatus from the Honduran mainland. Photograph by James R. McCranie

Similar species: *Coniophanes imperialis* has 19 dorsal scale rows at midbody and is recorded only from Utila and the Cayos Cochinos. *Leptodeira septentrionalis* has a dorsal pattern of spots or blotches, 170 or more ventral scales, and a vertically elliptical pupil. *Tantilla tritaeniata* has 15 dorsal scale rows throughout the body and is known only from Guanaja. *Tretanorhinus nigroluteus* has keeled dorsal scales and dorsolaterally placed nostrils.

General geographic distribution: Low and moderate elevations of the Atlantic versant from southern Veracruz, Mexico, to Panamá. In addition to Isla de Roatán, it also occurs on Isla Escudo de Veraguas, Panamá.

Distribution on Las Islas de la Bahía: *Coniophanes bipunctatus* occurs only on Roatán.

Natural history comments: *Coniophanes bipunctatus* is a nocturnal species that occurs in and around small streams on Roatán. L. Wilson and Hahn (1973) reported that none of their Roatán specimens were seen in the water, but we have subsequently collected specimens on that island that were in streams. The species occurs in hardwood forest on Roatán.

Coniophanes bipunctatus from Isla de Roatán. Photograph by Breck Bartholomew
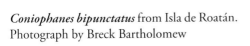

Coniophanes imperialis (Baird and Girard, *in* Baird, 1859)

Common name(s): Black-striped Snake (English; Liner, 1994).

Description: This snake is medium small (to about 550 mm TL), with a moderately long tail. The head is slightly distinct from the neck. The pupil is circular and 2 scales (a loreal and a preocular) are present between the postnasal and eye. Supralabials number 7 or 8, usually 8, with the fourth and fifth bordering the orbit. Infralabials number 8 to 10, usually 9 or 10. Ventrals range from 114 to 128 (114 to 141) and subcaudals from 69 to 88 (62 to 94). The cloacal scute is divided. Dorsal scales are smooth, without apical pits, in 19–19–17 or 19–19–15 rows. Ground color of the middorsum is tan to brown; the lower 3 to 5 rows are dark brown. A continuous or disjunct dark brown stripe extends along the middorsal scale row. A pale brown stripe on the head extends from the tip of the snout to the occipital region, where it may or may not be separate from a narrow, pale brown dorsolateral stripe separating the lateral and middorsal fields; in some cases, the pale head and dorsolateral body stripes are interrupted by an often-enlarged pale brown occipital spot. The venter is usually immaculate cream anteriorly, grading to pinkish orange posteriorly; occasionally, small, dark spots may be present on the anterior edges of the ventrals. The chin is dotted with small, dark brown spots.

Similar species: *Coniophanes bipunctatus* has 21 dorsal scale rows at midbody and is known only from Roatán. *Leptodeira septentrionalis* has a dorsal pattern of spots or blotches, 170 or more ventral scales, and a vertically elliptical pupil. *Tantilla tritaeniata* has 15 dorsal scale rows throughout the body and is known only from Guanaja.

General geographic distribution: Low and moderate elevations of the Atlantic versant from southern Texas, USA, to northeastern Honduras and on the Pacific versant in Oaxaca, Mexico.

Coniophanes imperialis from Isla de Utila.
Photograph by Gunther Köhler

Coniophanes imperialis from the Honduran mainland. Photograph by James R. McCranie

Distribution on Las Islas de la Bahía: *Coniophanes imperialis* is known from Utila and Cayo Cochino Pequeño.

Natural history comments: *Coniophanes imperialis* is primarily a diurnal species. The single specimen of the species from the Cayos Cochinos "was secured [during the day] in hill [hardwood] forest on Cayo Cochino Pequeño while it was crawling upon the litter of the forest floor" (L. Wilson and Cruz Díaz, 1993:18).

Coniophanes imperialis from Isla de Utila. Photograph by Breck Bartholomew

Dryadophis melanolomus (Cope, 1868)

Common name(s): Clap-and-saw-you (English), Clapansaya (corrupted English); Sumbadora (Spanish).

Description: This snake is moderately large (to about 1500 mm TL) with a moderately long (in females) to very long (in males) tail. The head is moderately set off from the neck. The pupil is circular and 2 scales (a loreal and a preocular) are present between the postnasal and eye. Supralabials number 8 to 10, usually 9, with the fourth, fifth, and sixth bordering the orbit. Infralabials number 8 to 11, usually 10. Ventrals range from 177 to 193 (160 to 195) and subcaudals from 91 to 114 (85 to 136). The cloacal scute is divided. Dorsal scales are smooth, with two apical pits, in 17–17–15 rows. The dorsum of the adults is brown. The venter is white or yellow to blue-green on the Cayos Cochinos and pearl gray on Utila, with the chin slightly paler. Supralabials are cream. The iris is rust red. The coloration of the juveniles consists of alternating dark brown-edged brown dorsal and lateral blotches on a pale brown background. The pale interspaces decrease in length and intensity posteriorly. The head is brown above with dark brown pre- and postocular stripes. The supralabials are pale cream with brown edging. The chin is white with brown spotting.

Similar species: *Drymarchon melanurus* is a larger snake and has an olive green dorsum grading to black on the posterior portion of the body and tail, a diagonal black mark on the neck, and a single cloacal scute. *Leptophis mexicanus* has a bright green head, a dark lateral stripe, and the dorsal scales in 15–15–11 rows.

General geographic distribution: Low and moderate elevations from southern Tamaulipas, Mexico, on the Atlantic versant and southern Sinaloa, Mexico, on the Pacific versant to central Panamá. In addition to the Cayos Cochinos and Isla de Utila, it also occurs on several Pacific islands off the coast of Costa Rica and Panamá.

Dryadophis melanolomus from Cayo Cochino Pequeño. Photograph by Mikael Lundberg

Dryadophis melanolomus from the Honduran mainland. Photograph by James R. McCranie

Distribution on Las Islas de la Bahía: *Dryadophis melanolomus* is recorded from Utila, Cayo Cochino Grande, and Cayo Cochino Pequeño.

Natural history comments: *Dryadophis melanolomus* is a diurnal, largely terrestrial species. L. Wilson and Cruz Díaz (1993) reported that all but one of their specimens from the Cayos Cochinos came from hardwood forest, with one exception coming from a coconut grove just behind East End Village. These authors also noted that one specimen was climbing the trunk of an oak tree. On Utila, this species has been seen on the ground and among rocks of a rocky outcrop in hardwood forest. It is a rapidly moving species that is difficult to capture when active on the ground.

Dryadophis melanolomus from Cayo Cochino Pequeño. Photograph by Mikael Lundberg

Drymarchon melanurus (Duméril, Bibron, and Duméril, 1854)

Common name(s): Clap-and-saw-you (English), Clapansaya (corrupted English); Sumbadora (Spanish).

Description: This snake is very large (to 2950 mm TL) with a moderately long tail. The head is moderately set off from the neck. The pupil is circular and 2 scales (a loreal and a preocular) are present between the postnasal and eye. Supralabials number 7 to 9, usually 8, with the fourth and fifth bordering the orbit. Infralabials number 7 to 10, usually 8. Ventrals range from 193 to 207 (182 to 215) and subcaudals from 68 to 80 (55 to 88). The cloacal scute is entire. Dorsal scales are smooth, with two apical pits, in 19 to 17 rows anteriorly, 17 rows at midbody, and 13 to 15 rows posteriorly. Dorsum is olive green, usually grading to black on the posterior portion of the body and the tail. A diagonal black mark about one and one-half scales long begins on about the fifth scale row on the neck and extends onto the lateral portion of the ventrals. The anterior venter is pale yellow, with a few black markings on the lateral edges of some of the ventral scales, gradually becoming increasingly infused with black near the vent. The head is olive green, with black pigment on the posterior edges of supralabials 4, 5, 6, and 7. The chin is cream, save for the posterior edges of infralabials 4, 5, and 6, which are black.

Similar species: *Dryadophis melanolomus* has a brown to gray-brown dorsum and a divided cloacal scute, and lacks a diagonal black mark on the neck.

General geographic distribution: Low, moderate, and occasionally intermediate elevations from south-central Texas, USA, on the Atlantic versant and from southern Sonora, Mexico, on the Pacific versant to northern Venezuela and northwestern Perú. It also occurs on Islas de Tres Marías, Nayarit, Mexico.

Distribution on Las Islas de la Bahía: *Drymarchon melanurus* is known from Guanaja, Roatán, and Utila.

Drymarchon melanurus from Isla de Guanaja. Photograph by Mikael Lundberg

Drymarchon melanurus from the Honduran mainland. Photograph by James R. McCranie

Natural history comments: *Drymarchon melanurus* is a terrestrial, diurnal snake that occurs in hardwood forest on the Bay Islands. The species appears to be rarely encountered on the Bay Islands.

Remarks: L. Wilson and Hahn (1973) included this species under the name *Drymarchon corais*.

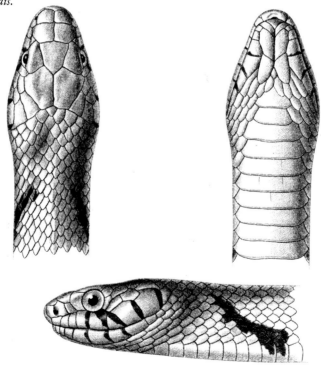

Head of *Drymarchon melanurus* as illustrated in A.H.A. Duméril, Bocourt, and Mocquard (1870–1909).

Enulius bifoveatus McCranie and Köhler, 1999

Common name(s): Guanaja Longtail Snake (English*).

Description: This snake is small (to about 320 mm TL) with a very long, thick tail. The head is barely distinct from the neck. The pupil is circular and only 1 scale is present between the postnasal and eye. Supralabials number 7, with the third and fourth bordering the orbit and infralabials number 5 or 6. Ventrals range from 168 to 181 and 120 subcaudals are present in the only known specimen with a complete tail (a male). The cloacal scute is divided. Dorsal scales are smooth, with paired apical pits, and in 17–17–15 rows. Dorsal coloration is uniformly dark purplish brown, grading to pale purple laterally on dorsal scale rows 2 to 4 on the body. A yellow nuchal collar is present, which may be completely or partially divided medially. Ventral surfaces are dirty white anteriorly, grading to pale brown at about midbody.

Similar species: Two other species of the genus *Enulius* occur on the Bay Islands. *Enulius flavitorques*, however, is recorded only from Utila and possesses single apical pits. *Enulius roatanensis* is known only from Roatán and possesses single apical pits, and also lacks a pale nuchal collar. No other snake on the Bay Islands has a unicolor dorsal coloration and an extremely long, thick tail.

General geographic distribution: *Enulius bifoveatus* is endemic to Isla de Guanaja.

Distribution on Las Islas de la Bahía: The species is known only from the northern portion of Guanaja.

Natural history comments: *Enulius bifoveatus* is a semifossorial species that has been taken in rotting, standing, or prone coconut palm trunks and under a log in a grassy area.

Enulius bifoveatus from Isla de Guanaja.
Photograph by James R. McCranie.

Enulius bifoveatus from Isla de Guanaja.
Photograph by James R. McCranie

Enulius bifoveatus from Isla de Guanaja.
Photograph by Gunther Köhler

Enulius flavitorques (Cope, "1868" [1869])

Common name(s): Longtail Snake (English*).

Description: This snake is small (to 500 mm TL) with a very long, thick tail. The head is barely distinct from the neck. The pupil is circular and only 1 scale is present between the postnasal and eye. Supralabials number 7 or 8, usually 7, with the third and fourth bordering the orbit. Infralabials number 6 to 8, usually 7. Ventrals range from 178 to 211 (166 to 216) and subcaudals from 89 to 114 (85 to 117). The cloacal scute is divided. Dorsal scales are smooth, with one apical pit, in 15–15–15, 15–17–17, 17–17–17, or 17–17–15 rows. Dorsal coloration is uniformly dark brown to black, although the ventral coloration extends upward to dorsal scale rows 2 or 3. A pale cream or yellow nuchal collar is present in all Honduran specimens. Ventral surfaces are white to cream.

Similar species: *Enulius bifoveatus* possesses two apical pits on most dorsal scales and is known only from Guanaja. *Enulius roatanensis* lacks a pale nuchal collar and is recorded only from Roatán. No other snake on the Bay Islands has a unicolor dorsal coloration and an extremely long, thick tail.

General geographic distribution: Low and moderate elevations of the Pacific versant from southern Jalisco, Mexico, to Panamá. It also occurs on the Atlantic versant in Chiapas, Mexico, Honduras, southwestern Nicaragua, Panamá, northern Colombia, and northwestern Venezuela.

Distribution on Las Islas de la Bahía: *Enulius flavitorques* is known only from Utila.

Natural history comments: The only Bay Island specimen of *Enulius flavitorques* was taken in sand next to a clutch of *Cnemidophorus lemniscatus* eggs in an area with coconut palms (A. Gutsche, pers. comm.). The lizard eggs were 35 cm deep in the sand (Gutsche, 2003).

Enulius flavitorques from Costa Rica.
Photograph by Louis W. Porras

Enulius flavitorques from the Honduran mainland. Photograph by James R. McCranie

Enulius flavitorques from Panamá. Photograph by Alan P. Jaslo

Enulius roatanensis McCranie and Köhler, 1999

Common name(s): Roatan Longtail Snake (English*).

Description: This snake is small (to about 345 mm TL) with a very long, thick tail. The head is barely distinct from the neck. The pupil is circular and only 1 scale is present between the postnasal and eye. Supralabials number 7, with third and fourth bordering the orbit and infralabials number 6. Ventrals range from 165 to 176 and subcaudals from 103 to 121. The cloacal scute is divided. Dorsal scales are smooth with a single apical pit, and in 17–17–17 rows. Dorsal coloration of the body and tail is blackish gray to dark grayish brown, gradually becoming paler laterally. The dorsal surface of the head is dark brown to rust brown. No nuchal collar is present, although the yellow color of the supralabials extends upward to the lower second temporal. Ventral surfaces are pale gray to white.

Similar species: *Enulius bifoveatus* has paired apical pits on most dorsal body scales and is restricted in distribution to Guanaja. *Enulius flavitorques* possesses a pale nuchal collar and is recorded only from Utila in the Bay Islands. No other snake on the Bay Islands has a unicolor dorsal coloration and an extremely long, thick tail.

General geographic distribution: *Enulius roatanensis* is endemic to Isla de Roatán.

Distribution on Las Islas de la Bahía: The species is known only from the western portion of Isla de Roatán.

Natural history comments: This semifossorial species has been found in a rotting, standing coconut palm trunk and crawling at night in low vegetation on a road cut. Habitat types include hardwood forest and coconut groves.

Remarks: L. Wilson and Hahn (1973) included this snake under the name *Enulius flavitorques*.

Enulius roatanensis from Isla de Roatán.
Photograph by Gunther Köhler.

Imantodes cenchoa (Linnaeus, 1758)

Common name(s): Blunthead Tree Snake (English; Liner, 1994).

Description: This snake is moderately-sized (to 1250 mm TL), very elongate, and slender, with a long tail. The blunt head is very distinctly set off from the neck. The pupil is vertically elliptical and 2 scales (a loreal and a preocular) are present between the postnasal and eye. Supralabials number 7 to 9, usually 8, with the fourth and fifth, third, fourth, and fifth, or fourth, fifth, and sixth bordering the orbit. Infralabials number 9 to 12, usually 10. Ventrals range from 228 to 261 (228 to 288) and subcaudals from 134 to 170 (134 to 195). The cloacal scute is divided. Dorsal scales are smooth, without apical pits, in 19–17–17, 17–17–17, or 17–17–15 rows. The vertebral dorsal scale row is conspicuously enlarged, about 3 to 5 times the size of the lateral body scales. Dorsum of the body and tail is beige with dark brown-outlined brown blotches. The venter is pale pinkish tan with extensive dark brown flecking. The head is brown and the iris olive green.

Similar species: No other snake in the area is likely to be confused with this extremely slender, elongate, blunt-headed snake with large, bulging eyes. *Pseudelaphe flavirufa*, however, has a considerably less slender body and 27 to 34 dorsal scale rows at midbody and *Leptodeira septentrionalis* has fewer than 215 ventral and 110 subcaudal scales, and 19 to 23 dorsal scale rows at midbody.

General geographic distribution: Low, moderate, and intermediate elevations of the Atlantic versant from southern Tamaulipas, Mexico, to northeastern Argentina and the Pacific versant from southeastern Chiapas, Mexico, to Guatemala and from northwestern Costa Rica (exclusive of the Pacific lowlands) to northwestern Ecuador. It also occurs on Isla del Venado, Nicaragua, Isla del Rey (Islas del Perlas), Panamá, and the islands of Trinidad and Tobago.

Distribution on Las Islas de la Bahía: *Imantodes cenchoa* is known only from Utila.

Natural history comments: Nothing is known about the natural history of *Imantodes cenchoa* on the Bay Islands. However, on the Honduran mainland, it is an arboreal, nocturnal species found in forested areas. Thus, it probably occurs in hardwood forest on the Bay Islands.

Imantodes cenchoa from the Honduran mainland. Photograph by James R. McCranie.

Leptodeira septentrionalis (Kennicott, *in* Baird, 1859)

Common name(s): Cat-eyed Snake (English*).

Description: This snake is medium-sized to medium large (to 1055 mm TL) with a moderate to long tail. The head is distinctly set off from the neck. The pupil is vertically elliptical and 2 scales (a loreal and a preocular) are present between the postnasal and eye. Supralabials number 7 to 9, usually 8, with the fourth and fifth bordering the orbit. Infralabials number 9 to 12, usually 10. Ventrals range from 189 to 206 (170 to 211) and subcaudals from 83 to 106 (60 to 107). The cloacal scute is divided. Dorsal scales are smooth, with two apical pits, usually in 21 or 23 rows at midbody and 15 or 17 rows at the vent. Dorsum of the body is cinnamon brown, with a series (20 to 70) of dark brown dorsal blotches. The venter is pale pinkish tan. The top of the head is brown and the chin is pale cream. The iris is copper.

Similar species: *Coniophanes bipunctatus* and *C. imperialis* have striped dorsal surfaces, fewer than 145 ventral scales, and circular pupils. *Imantodes cenchoa* is extremely slender with a blunt head well set off from the extremely slender neck, has 228 to 261 ventral scales, 134 to 170 subcaudal scales, and 17 dorsal scale rows at midbody.

General geographic distribution: Low, moderate, and intermediate elevations of the Atlantic versant from southern Texas, USA, to Perú. It is also discontinuously distributed on the Pacific versant from southern Sinaloa, Mexico, to Perú (see Remarks).

Distribution on Las Islas de la Bahía: *Leptodeira septentrionalis* is known from Cayo Cochino Pequeño.

Natural history comments: *Leptodeira septentrionalis* is a nocturnal and usually arboreal species. The single Islas de la Bahía specimen was taken about 2.5 m above the ground in an oak tree (*Quercus oleoides*; see Lundberg, 2002).

Remarks: More than one species may be included within the general geographic

Leptodeira septentrionalis from Cayo Cochino Pequeño. Photograph by Mikael Lundberg

Leptodeira septentrionalis from the Honduran mainland. Photograph by Mikael Lundberg

distribution given above. Savage (2002) briefly discussed this matter. Lundberg (2002) recently reported the species from Cayo Cochino Pequeño, the first record for Las Islas de la Bahía.

Leptodeira septentrionalis from the Honduran mainland. Photograph by James R. McCranie

Leptophis mexicanus Duméril, Bibron, and Duméril, 1854

Common name(s): Bronze-backed Snake (English*).

Description: This snake is medium large (to about 1270 mm TL) with a very long tail. The head is distinctly set off from the neck. The pupil is circular and 2 scales (a loreal and a preocular) are present between the postnasal and eye. Supralabials number 8 or 9, usually 8, with the fourth and fifth bordering the orbit. Infralabials number 9 to 11, usually 10. Ventrals range from 145 to 161 (145 to 183) and subcaudals from 141 to 166 (140 to 181). The cloacal scute is divided and the dorsal scales are keeled (except for the outer row), with a single apical pit, in 15–15–11 rows. The top of the head is iridescent emerald green grading to bronze on the middorsum of the body. The middorsal stripe is edged with iridescent blue-green. Scales of rows 3 to 5 are dull gold with black tips and blue-green bases, creating the impression of an irregular stripe. The black markings of this stripe coalesce on the neck to form a solid black stripe, which continues onto the temporal and preocular regions of the head. Scales of rows 1 and 2 are pale orange, although the upper edge of the scales of row 2 is black. The venter is pale bronze grading to white on the chin. The underside of the tail is pale golden bronze. The iris is yellow dorsally, black ventrally, the latter portion continuous with the preocular and temporal stripes.

Similar species: *Oxybelis fulgidus* has a uniform leaf-green dorsum, a distinctly attenuate head, and 17 dorsal scale rows at midbody.

General geographic distribution: Low and moderate elevations of the Atlantic versant from southern Tamaulipas, Mexico, to north-central Costa Rica and discontinuously distributed on the Pacific versant in Chiapas and eastern Oaxaca, Mexico, to central El Salvador, western Nicaragua, and northwestern Costa Rica. In addition to Isla de Utila, it also occurs on Islas del Maíz Grande, Nicaragua, and on several islands off the coast of Belize.

Distribution on Las Islas de la Bahía: *Leptophis mexicanus* occurs only on Utila.

Leptophis mexicanus from Honduras.
Photograph by Mikael Lundberg

Leptophis mexicanus from Isla de Utila.
Photograph by Gunther Köhler

Natural history comments: *Leptophis mexicanus* is a diurnal species that can be both terrestrial and arboreal. The species has been found on the Bay Islands while active on the ground in a banana clearing (carved from hardwood forest), foraging in low bushes, and while sleeping at night on top of grass in a swampy area. It is probably active throughout the year on Utila.

Leptophis mexicanus from Isla de Utila.
Photograph by Robert Powell

Oxybelis aeneus (Wagler, 1824)

Common name(s): Whipping Snake (English).

Description: This snake is moderately large (to 1700 mm TL) and very slender, with a very long, attenuate tail. The head is elongate, pointed, and distinctly set off from the neck. The pupil is circular and 2 scales (a preocular and a lateral extension of each prefrontal) are present between the nasal and eye. Supralabials number 6 to 10, usually 8 or 9, with the fourth, fifth, and sixth bordering the orbit. Infralabials number 6 to 11, usually 8 or 9. Ventrals range from 176 to 198 (173 to 205) and subcaudals from 166 to 197 (158 to 203). The cloacal scute is usually divided. Dorsal scales are smooth to weakly keeled, without apical pits, usually in 17–17–13 rows. Dorsum of the body is pale brown flecked with dark brown. The top of the head is reddish brown. Supralabials are pale yellow, edged dorsally by a thin dark grayish brown stripe. The venter is pale pinkish tan, with mahogany red smudging on the middle of the white chin and neck. The iris is pale iridescent bronze dorsally and olive green ventrally.

Similar species: *Oxybelis fulgidus* has a uniformly bright green dorsum and a pair of white to pale yellow ventrolateral stripes on the pale green to chartreuse venter. *Oxybelis wilsoni* has a uniformly mustard yellow dorsum and a pair of white ventrolateral stripes on a bright yellow venter.

General geographic distribution: Low, moderate, and occasionally intermediate elevations from south-central Nuevo León, Mexico, on the Atlantic versant and extreme southern Arizona, USA, on the Pacific versant to southern Brazil east of the Andes and northwestern Perú west of the Andes. In addition to the Bay Islands, it also occurs on numerous other islands, as follows: Islas Tres Marías, Nayarit, and Isla Mujeres, Quintana Roo, Mexico; Isla Zacate Grande, Honduras; Islas del Maíz, Nicaragua; Islas de Coiba and Perlas,

Oxybelis aeneus from the Honduran mainland.
Photograph by James R. McCranie.

Oxybelis aeneus from Isla de Guanaja.
Photograph by Mikael Lundberg

Panamá; Trinidad and Tobago; and several small islands off the coast of Venezuela.

   Distribution on Las Islas de la Bahía: *Oxybelis aeneus* is recorded from Barbareta, Guanaja, Roatán, Utila, and Cayo Cochino Grande.

   Natural history comments: *Oxybelis aeneus* is a diurnal, usually arboreal species. L. Wilson and Hahn (1973:130) described the natural history of this species on the Bay Islands as follows: "*O. aeneus* primarily inhabits edge situations, especially along pathways through the forest and in clearings, where it is found in low shrubs and occasionally on the ground. We collected one specimen in the grass of a cleared banana field, another on the ground in a coconut grove along the beach, and yet another in the grass of the front yard of La Playa Hotel on Guanaja. During a half-hour walk from the town of Sabana Bight to the air field on the other side of the island's north end we collected some 11 specimens in low bushes along the path." This species is probably active throughout the year on the Islas de la Bahía. Habitat types on the Bay Islands and Cayos Cochinos include hardwood forest and coconut groves (including beach area vegetation).

Oxybelis aeneus from Isla de Roatán.
Photograph by Mikael Lundberg

Oxybelis fulgidus (Daudin, 1803)

Common name(s): Green Tommygoff (English).

Description: This snake is large (to 2000 mm TL) and relatively slender, with a very long, attenuate tail. The head is elongate, pointed, and distinctly set off from the neck. The pupil is circular and 2 scales (a preocular and lateral extension of each prefrontal) are present between the nasal and eye. Supralabials number 9 to 12, usually 9 or 10, with the fourth, fifth, and sixth or fifth, sixth, and seventh bordering the orbit. Infralabials number 9 to 12, usually 10. Ventrals range from 201 to 216 (198 to 216) and subcaudals from 153 to 166 (133 to 171). The cloacal scute is usually divided. Dorsal scales are lightly keeled, without apical pits, in 17–17–13 rows. Dorsal coloration is bright green. Ventral coloration is yellowish green with a yellowish white line extending ventrolaterally on each side the length of the body, each extending onto the subcaudal surface. The head is green above with a dark green or black eye stripe. Supralabials and lower jaw are yellowish green.

Similar species: *Oxybelis aeneus* is a smaller, more slender snake with a pale brown dorsum flecked with dark brown. The dorsum of the head is reddish brown. The venter is pale pinkish tan and lacks pale lateral longitudinal ventrolateral stripes. *Oxybelis wilsoni* has a mustard yellow dorsum and bright yellow venter and is known to occur only on Roatán.

General geographic distribution: Low and moderate elevations of the Atlantic versant from the Yucatán Peninsula, Mexico, to the Amazonian Basin of southeastern Perú and central Brazil and on the Pacific versant from southeastern Oaxaca, Mexico, to north-central Costa Rica and in eastern Panamá. An apparently isolated population also occurs in southern Veracruz, Mexico. It also occurs on Isla de Patos, Venezuela.

Distribution on Las Islas de la Bahía: *Oxybelis fulgidus* occurs only on Utila.

Natural history comments: *Oxybelis fulgidus* is a diurnal, largely arboreal species. L. Wilson and Hahn (1973:131) collected an adult "from brush along the beach." Another was found on Utila as it caught and swallowed a mouse (Köhler, 2003).

Oxybelis fulgidus from Costa Rica.
Photograph by Alejandro Solórzano

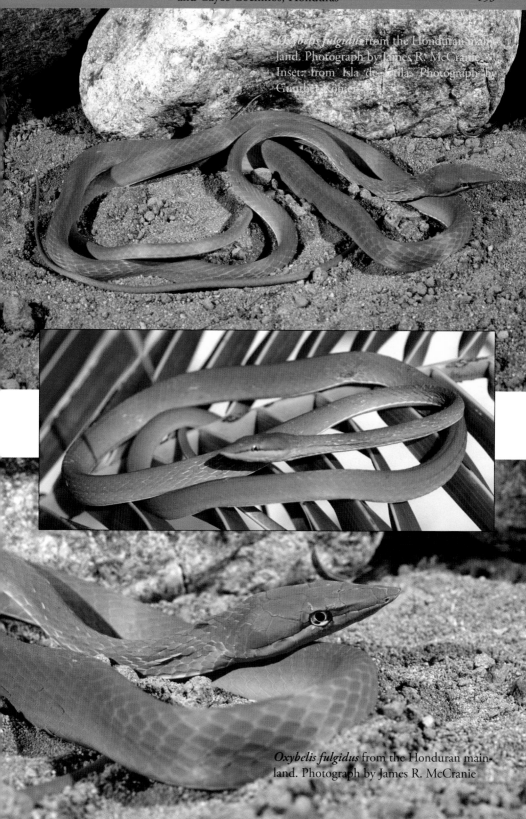

Oxybelis fulgidus from the Honduran mainland. Photograph by James R. McCranie. Inset: from Isla de Utila. Photograph by Gunther Köhler.

Oxybelis fulgidus from the Honduran mainland. Photograph by James R. McCranie

Oxybelis wilsoni Villa and McCranie, 1995

Common name(s): Yellow Snake (English).

Description: This snake is large (to about 2000 mm TL) and relatively slender, with a very long, attenuate tail. The head is elongate, pointed, and distinctly set off from the neck. The pupil is circular and 2 scales (a preocular and a lateral extension of each prefrontal) are present between the nasal and eye. Supralabials number 9 to 12, usually 10, with the fifth, sixth, and seventh or sixth, seventh, and eighth bordering the orbit. Infralabials number 9 to 12, usually 10 or 11. Ventrals range from 201 to 217 and subcaudals from 164 to 189. The cloacal scute is divided. Dorsal scales are weakly keeled (on about the 6 median rows) to smooth, without apical pits, and in 17–17–13 rows. The dorsum is mustard yellow. The venter is pale yellow medially, pale tan laterally, and with these two areas divided by a narrow white ventrolateral stripe extending the length of the body. The head is mustard yellow above and bright yellow on the supralabials and chin. The iris is yellow.

Similar species: *Oxybelis aeneus* is a smaller, more slender snake with a pale brown dorsum flecked with dark brown. The top of the head is reddish brown. The venter is pale pinkish tan to tan and lacks pale lateral stripes. *Oxybelis fulgidus* has a uniformly bright green dorsum and is known only from Utila.

General geographic distribution: *Oxybelis wilsoni* is endemic to Isla de Roatán.

Distribution on Las Islas de la Bahía: See General geographic distribution.

Natural history comments: Villa and McCranie (1995:301) provided the following: "*Oxybelis wilsoni* is primarily arboreal, but can occasionally be found on the ground. Only two specimens of the large series recently collected (both juveniles) were taken on the ground. The remaining specimens were found waist-height to about 10 m above the ground in tall grasses, bushes, and trees. Another indication of the arboreal tendencies of this species

Oxybelis wilsoni from Isla de Roatán.
Photograph by James R. McCranie

Oxybelis wilsoni from Isla de Roatán.
Photograph by Breck Bartholomew

is that specimens dislodged from their arboreal perches would, upon hitting the ground, immediately raise their bodies upward searching for the nearest object to climb instead of trying to escape on the ground. This was done even in areas where tall grasses would make escape relatively easy. One specimen that landed next to where McCranie was standing emerged from the waist high grass and attempted to climb up his body. The species was commonly found in *Acacia* bushes growing alongside roads between Coxen Hole and West End and east of Oak Ridge, as well as in various trees used as fencerows along these same roads. The species was also collected in fencerows in pastures on the hillsides above Coxen Hole. A single specimen was found in an isolated ironwood tree (*Laplacea* sp.) in a pasture near the western tip of Isla de Roatán. On the eastern end of the island (Santa Elena), the species was found in buttonwood (*Conocarpus erectus*) and sea grape trees (*Coccoloba* sp.). L. Wilson and Hahn (1973:131) also stated the 'one specimen was collected high in a mango tree and another about 3 meters up in a tree' near Coxen Hole. These authors also reported that a single 'road kill' carcass was also found." Habitat types include hardwood forest and beach area vegetation.

Remarks: L. Wilson and Hahn (1973) included this species under the name *Oxybelis fulgidus*.

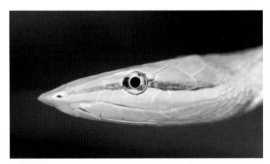

Oxybelis wilsoni from Isla de Roatán.
Photograph by Breck Bartholomew

Pseudelaphe flavirufa (Cope, "1866" [1867])

Common name(s): Nightwalker (English).

Description: This snake is large (to about 1650 mm TL) with a moderately long tail. The head is distinctly set off from the neck. The pupil is circular and 2 scales (a loreal and a preocular) are present between the postnasal and eye. Supralabials number 8 to 10, usually 9, with the fourth, fifth, and sixth bordering the orbit. Infralabials number 12 to 15, usually 12 or 13. Ventrals range from 258 to 269 (245 to 269) and subcaudals from 100 to 122 (96 to 122). The cloacal scute is divided. Dorsal scales are smooth to about row 7, then faintly keeled from that point upward, in 25 to 31 rows anteriorly, 27 to 34 at midbody, and 19 to 25 posteriorly. Dorsal ground color is yellowish tan to gray, with a series of 37 to 46 (29 to 46) reddish brown, rust, or brick red middorsal blotches, each outlined with dark brown or black and yellowish cream; posterior blotches may be fused into a zigzag stripe. A series of smaller lateral and ventrolateral blotches is also present. The venter is cream colored with a few squarish pale brown or brownish gray blotches present. The head is grayish tan dorsally, with a few scattered dark markings. The chin is white with a few dark reddish brown markings. The iris is gray.

Similar species: All other colubrids from the Islas de la Bahía have 15 to 23 dorsal scale rows at midbody.

General geographic distribution: Low elevations of the Atlantic versant from central Tamaulipas, Mexico, to north-central Honduras and on the Pacific versant in eastern Oaxaca and southern Chiapas, Mexico, and western Nicaragua. In addition to the Bay Islands, it also occurs on Isla del Maíz Grande, Nicaragua.

Distribution on Las Islas de la Bahía: *Pseudelaphe flavirufa* is recorded from Guanaja, Roatán, and Utila.

Pseudelaphe flavirufa from Isla de Utila.
Photograph by Gunther Köhler.

Pseudelaphe flavirufa from Isla de Utila. Photograph by Robert Powell

Natural history comments: *Pseudelaphe flavirufa* is a nocturnal, semi-arboreal species. On the Bay Islands, it has been taken in a tree along a road, in an attic of a house, stretched out on a barbed-wire fence, under debris on the floor of an abandoned stilt house, and in piles of lumber in an open building. Köhler (1998a) also reported on two shed skins of this snake that were found in a storage shed. Habitat types on the Bay Islands include hardwood forest, coconut groves (including beach area vegetation), and urban areas.

Remarks: Smith and Williams (1966a) proposed the new subspecific name *Elaphe flavirufa polysticha* for a single specimen of this snake collected on Roatán in the late 1800s. L. Wilson and Hahn (1973), after examining additional Bay Island specimens, as well as specimens from the mainland, concluded that recognizing a Bay Island subspecies was not warranted. All recent literature mentioning this species from the Bay Islands included it under the generic name *Elaphe*.

Pseudelaphe flavirufa from Isla de Utila. Photograph by Robert Powell

Tantilla tritaeniata **Smith and Williams, 1966b**

Common name(s): Striped Ground Snake (English*).

Description: This snake is small (to 273 mm TL) with a moderately long tail. The head is slightly distinct from the neck. The pupil is circular and only 1 scale is present between the postnasal and eye. Supralabials number 7, with the third and fourth bordering the orbit. Infralabials number 6. Ventrals range from 155 to 161 and subcaudals from 59 to 65. The cloacal scute is divided or entire. Dorsal scales are smooth, without apical pits, in 15 rows throughout the body. Dorsum is brown with orangish brown middorsal and cream lateral stripes. A middorsal stripe occupies the middorsal row and adjacent two-thirds of the paravertebral rows along the length of the body, not narrowing anteriorly, and beginning on the third dorsal scale row posterior to the parietals (as do the lateral stripes). The head is brown above and a middorsally-divided or middorsally- and laterally-divided pale brown nuchal band is present. The venter is immaculate cream.

Similar species: No other species of snake in the area is likely to be confused with this small snake with three pale stripes on a dark ground color and a middorsally divided pale nuchal collar. The only other small snake known from Guanaja is *Enulius bifoveatus*, which has a uniformly dark dorsal body coloration, 17 dorsal scale rows throughout the body, and a very long and relatively thick tail. *Coniophanes bipunctatus* and *C. imperialis* have longitudinal stripes, but have 21 and 19 dorsal scale rows at midbody, respectively. In addition, *C. bipunctatus* is known only from Roatán and *C. imperialis* from Utila and the Cayos Cochinos.

General geographic distribution: *Tantilla tritaeniata* is endemic to Isla de Guanaja.

Distribution on Las Islas de la Bahía: See General geographic distribution.

Tantilla tritaeniata from Isla de Guanaja.
Photograph by James R. McCranie.

Tantilla tritaeniata from Isla de Guanaja.
Photograph by James R. McCranie

Natural history comments: *Tantilla tritaeniata* has been collected inside the base of a standing, rotting coconut palm stump. Another was found dead along a stream running through a coconut grove on a beach.

Remarks: This species was recently resurrected from the synonymy of the mainland species *Tantilla taeniata* by L. Wilson and McCranie (1999). L. Wilson and Hahn (1973) included this species under the name *T. taeniata*.

Tantilla tritaeniata from Isla de Guanaja.
Photograph by James R. McCranie

Tretanorhinus nigroluteus Cope, "1861" (1862a)

Common name(s): Water Snake (English); Culebra de Agua (Spanish).

Description: This snake is medium-sized (to about 885 mm TL) with a moderately long tail. The head is distinctly set off from the neck. Nostrils are dorsolaterally placed. The pupil is vertically elliptical and 2 scales (a loreal and a preocular) are present between the postnasal and eye. Supralabials number 7 to 9, usually 8, with the fourth (infrequently the fourth and fifth) bordering the orbit. Infralabials number 9 to 11, usually 10. Ventrals range from 130 to 152 (127 to 152) and subcaudals from 57 to 82 (56 to 82). The cloacal scute is divided. Dorsal scales are keeled, without apical pits, usually in 21–21–19 or 21–21–17 rows (but also showing considerable variation; anterior count either 21 or 23; midbody count 19, 21, or 23; posterior count 15, 17, or 19). Dorsal ground color is pale brown or olive brown to black, with or without a pale lateral stripe on the third and fourth scale rows, and with or without a double series of paravertebral and dorsolateral blotches; paravertebral blotches sometimes are fused into an irregular stripe on some or all of the body. The venter is either reddish orange to red or pale tan, with or without midventral black mottling.

Similar species: Only *Coniophanes bipunctatus* occupies a similar microhabitat (i.e., streams and streamsides), but it possesses smooth dorsal scales and laterally placed nostrils.

General geographic distribution: Low and moderate elevations of the Atlantic versant from central Veracruz, Mexico, to northern Colombia and on the Pacific versant in south-central Honduras and western Nicaragua. In addition to the Bay Islands, it also occurs on Isla del Maíz Grande, Nicaragua.

Distribution on Las Islas de la Bahía: *Tretanorhinus nigroluteus* is recorded from Guanaja, Roatán, and Utila.

Natural history comments: *Tretanorhinus nigroluteus* is a nocturnal, aquatic snake. On the Bay Islands, this species is active in streams through hardwood forest, although it can occasionally be found in swampy areas.

Tretanorhinus nigroluteus from Isla de Roatán.
Photograph by James R. McCranie.

Tretanorhinus nigroluteus from Isla de Guanaja.
Photograph by Mikael Lundberg

Remarks: Villa (1969) described the Roatán and Guanaja specimens as a new subspecies, *Tretanorhinus nigroluteus dichromaticus*. L. Wilson and Hahn (1973) demonstrated that no subspecies of *T. nigroluteus* should be recognized.

Tretanorhinus nigroluteus from Isla de Roatán.
Photograph by James R. McCranie

Family Elapidae

Elapids are venomous and have proteroglyph dentition on a relatively rigid maxilla. The members of this family of snakes range in the Western Hemisphere from the southern USA through Mexico and Central America, and into South America as far south as Perú (both west and east of the Andes), central Argentina, southeastern Brazil, and Uruguay. Members also are broadly distributed in the Eastern Hemisphere, occurring throughout Africa, the Arabian Peninsula, the southern Middle East, the Near East, the Indian subcontinent, southeastern Asia, China, Malaysia, Indonesia, Papua New Guinea, Taiwan, Japan, Australia, and the Solomon Islands. Sea snakes are found in the waters of the Indian and Pacific Oceans. Sixty genera containing 298 species were included in this family by David and Ineich (1999) and approximately 62 genera with 300 species by Pough et al. (2003). Two genera comprising six species are currently known to occur in Honduras. One endemic species occurs on the Bay Islands.

Micrurus ruatanus (Günther, 1895)

Common name(s): Babaspul (corrupted English); Coral (Spanish).

Description: This coral snake is medium small (to 681 mm TL) with a short tail. The head is only slightly distinct from the neck. The pupil is subcircular and only 1 scale is present between the postnasal and eye. Supralabials number 7, with the third and fourth bordering the orbit. Infralabials number 7. Ventrals range from 183 to 203 and subcaudal scales from 34 to 47. The cloacal scute is divided. Dorsal scales are smooth, save for the presence of para-cloacal tubercles in males, without apical pits, and in 15 rows throughout the body. Dorsum of the body is dark red with a series of 33 to 45 black rings. Black rings of about three scales in length alternate with those of one to two scales in length, a pattern being more pronounced on the posterior portion of the body; the narrower rings are frequently

Micrurus ruatanus from Isla de Roatán.
Photograph by James R. McCranie

Micrurus ruatanus from Isla de Roatán.
Photograph by James R. McCranie.

interrupted laterally. The snout is black to slightly beyond the juncture of the prefrontals or the frontal and supraoculars. A dark red nuchal band follows and is, in turn, followed by the first black body ring, which begins one to one and one-half scales posterior to the parietals.

Similar species: No other snake known from Las Islas de la Bahía has a pattern of red and black rings on the body, so this snake cannot be confused with any other.

General geographic distribution: *Micrurus ruatanus* is endemic to Isla de Roatán.

Distribution on Las Islas de la Bahía: See General geographic distribution.

Natural history comments: *Micrurus ruatanus* is a semifossorial species that is probably both diurnal and nocturnal. It has been found under piles of coconut fronds, under a board near a trash pile, and moving about in the open shortly after dawn in hardwood forest.

Remarks: One of the more interesting and inventive myths is alluded to in the species account of *Bufo marinus* (see p. 35) and involves toads and venomous snakes. Some people on the Bay Islands believe that no venomous snakes occurred on these islands because no toads were present (L. Wilson and Hahn, 1973). They think that venomous snakes are able to sequester the toxins that toads possess, making them venomous also. Thus, the venomous snake present on Roatán, *Micrurus ruatanus*, is thought not to be so. *Micrurus ruatanus* appears to be a rare snake, so it may be that people do not encounter them often, reducing the chances that the true nature of this coral snake would be revealed. In addition, we know of no record of a bite of a human by this snake. Nonetheless, *Micrurus ruatanus* is a venomous coral snake and caution should be exercised in dealing with it. The best policy is to leave the animal alone. It is endemic to the Bay Islands, so it is ill advised to harm it. In general, no snake is capable of sequestering amphibian toxins for its own use, i.e., transporting the toxin of a food organism to a portion of the body of the predator for use in its own protection. Venomous coral snakes possess their own venom glands located on either side of the temporal region of the head. It is venom from these glands that venomous snakes deliver in a bite. The story related above in the remarks section of the *Bufo marinus* account involves

Micrurus ruatanus from Isla de Roatán.
Photograph by James R. McCranie.

a curious reversal of circumstances. Now that this toad has been introduced on Guanaja and is breeding there, at least one individual is concerned that the island's snakes will now become venomous from eating the toad. This will not occur, as explained above. Also, none of the snakes known to inhabit Guanaja are noted for eating toads.

Micrurus ruatanus from Isla de Roatán.
Photograph by Breck Bartholomew

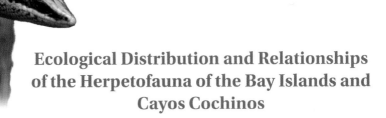

Ecological Distribution and Relationships of the Herpetofauna of the Bay Islands and Cayos Cochinos

The islands of the Honduran department of Islas de la Bahía are of varying sizes, have differing geological histories, physiographies, and relationships to the mainland of Honduras, and possess differing groupings of amphibians and reptiles with divergent ecological requirements, so it should come as no surprise that individual species do not range into all of the habitats present on these islands. Rather, various patterns of ecological distribution and relationships of the members of the island herpetofauna are observed.

Nine major habitat types are recognized (i.e., hardwood forest, pine forest, mangrove forest, coconut groves, ironshore formations, swamps and marches, estuaries, marine environments, and urban settings). The distribution of the 55 island species in these nine habitat types is indicated in Table 3. The largest number of species (38 or 69.1% of the total) is found in hardwood forest. This situation is to be expected, given the relative hospitability of this habitat type for amphibians and reptiles. The respective numbers found in the other eight habitat types are, in descending order, as follows: coconut groves—20 or 36.4%; swamps and marshes—11 or 20.0%; mangrove forest—10 or 18.2%; urban settings—10 or 18.2%; ironshore formations—4 or 7.3%; pine forest—3 or 5.5%; estuaries—3 or 5.5%; marine environments—3 or 5.5%. In general, the species numbers are lower in habitat types less hospitable to amphibians and reptiles or that are more specialized (e.g., estuaries or marine habitats).

Members of the island herpetofauna occupy from one to seven habitat types, with a mean occupancy figure of 1.9. Thus, the average species occurs typically in more than one habitat type. The most broadly distributed species is *Basiliscus vittatus* in seven of nine habitat types, followed by *Phyllodactylus palmeus* in five habitat types.

In order to determine the relationships of the herpetofaunas of these various habitat types to one another, we constructed a table of Coefficients of Habitat Resemblance (CHR), based on the formula used to determine Coefficient of Biogeographic Resemblance (CBR) values (see section on Biogeographic Relationships, page 169). The marine habitat is not included, inasmuch as the three marine turtles occur in no other habitat type. These CHR values are indicated in Table 4.

A relatively broad range of CHR values are seen in Table 4, from 0.00 to 0.48. The average value is 0.19. Ranges and average values for each habitat type are as follows: hardwood forest—0.00–0.48 (0.25); pine forest—0.00–0.33 (0.22); mangrove forest—0.10–0.33 (0.26); coconut groves—0.00–0.48 (0.22); ironshore formations—0.00–0.29 (0.18); swamps and marshes—0.00–0.37 (0.17); estuaries—0.00–0.20 (0.05); urban settings—0.00–0.33 (0.23). Using the average values, hardwood forests, pine forest, mangrove forests, coconut groves, and urban areas show more resemblance to other habitat types than

Table 3. Distribution of the Herpetofauna in the Habitat Types of the Bay Islands and Cayos Cochinos

Species	Hardwood Forest	Pine Forest	Mangrove Forest	Coconut Groves[1]	Ironshore Formation	Swamps & Marshes	Estuaries	Marine	Urban	Totals
Bufo marinus	—	—	—	—	—	X	—	—	X	2
Hyla microcephala	X	—	—	—	—	X	—	—	—	2
Scinax staufferi	X	—	—	—	—	X	—	—	—	2
Smilisca baudinii	X	—	—	—	—	X	—	—	—	2
Leptodactylus melanonotus	X	X	—	—	—	X	—	—	—	3
Rana berlandieri	X	—	—	—	—	X	—	—	—	2
Rana vaillanti	—	—	—	—	—	X	—	—	—	1
Crocodylus acutus	—	—	X	—	—	—	X	—	—	2
Caretta caretta	—	—	—	—	—	—	—	X	—	1
Chelonia mydas	—	—	—	—	—	—	—	X	—	1
Eretmochelys imbricata	—	—	—	—	—	—	—	X	—	1
Trachemys venusta	—	—	—	—	—	—	X	—	—	1
Kinosternon leucostomum	—	—	—	—	—	—	X	—	—	1
Coleonyx mitratus	X	—	—	—	—	—	—	—	X	2
Hemidactylus frenatus	—	—	—	—	—	—	—	—	X	1
Phyllodactylus palmeus	X	X	X	X	—	—	—	—	X	5
Sphaerodactylus millepunctatus	X	—	—	X	—	—	—	—	X	3
Sphaerodactylus rosaurae	X	—	X	X	—	—	—	—	—	3
Thecadactylus rapicauda	X	—	—	—	—	—	—	—	—	1
Basiliscus vittatus	X	X	X	X	X	X	—	—	X	7
Ctenosaura bakeri	—	—	X	X	—	—	—	—	—	2
Ctenosaura melanosterna	X	—	—	—	X	—	—	—	—	2
Ctenosaura oedirhina	X	—	X	X	X	—	—	—	—	4
Ctenosaura similis	X	—	X	—	—	—	—	—	X	3
Iguana iguana	X	—	—	—	—	X	—	—	—	2
Anolis allisoni	X	—	—	X	—	—	—	—	X	3
Norops bicaorum	X	—	X	—	—	—	—	—	—	2

Table 3. (continued) Distribution of the Herpetofauna in the Habitat Types of the Bay Islands and Cayos Cochinos

Species	Hardwood Forest	Pine Forest	Mangrove Forest	Coconut Groves[1]	Ironshore Formation	Swamps & Marshes	Estuaries	Marine	Urban	Totals
Norops lemurinus	X	—	—	—	—	—	—	—	—	1
Norops roatanensis	X	—	—	—	—	—	—	—	—	1
Norops sagrei	—	—	—	—	—	—	—	—	X	1
Norops sericeus	X	—	—	—	—	—	—	—	—	1
Norops utilensis	—	—	X	—	—	—	—	—	—	1
Mabuya unimarginata	X	—	—	X	—	—	—	—	—	2
Sphenomorphus cherriei	X	—	—	—	—	—	—	—	—	1
Gymnophthalmus speciosus	X	—	—	X	—	—	—	—	—	2
Cnemidophorus lemniscatus	—	—	—	X	—	—	—	—	—	1
Leptotyphlops goudotii	X	—	—	—	X	—	—	—	—	2
Boa constrictor	X	—	X	—	—	—	—	—	—	2
Coniophanes bipunctatus	X	—	—	—	—	—	—	—	—	1
Coniophanes imperialis	X	—	—	—	—	—	—	—	—	1
Dryadophis melanolomus	X	—	—	X	—	—	—	—	—	2
Drymarchon melanurus	X	—	—	—	—	—	—	—	—	1
Enulius bifoveatus	—	—	—	X	—	—	—	—	—	1
Enulius flavitorques	—	—	—	X	—	—	—	—	—	1
Enulius roatanensis	X	—	—	X	—	—	—	—	—	2
Imantodes cenchoa	X	—	—	—	—	—	—	—	—	1
Leptodeira septentrionalis	X	—	—	—	—	—	—	—	—	1
Leptophis mexicanus	X	—	—	—	—	X	—	—	—	2
Oxybelis aeneus	X	—	—	X	—	—	—	—	—	2
Oxybelis fulgidus	—	—	—	X	—	—	—	—	—	1
Oxybelis wilsoni	X	—	—	X	—	—	—	—	—	2
Pseudelaphe flavirufa	X	—	—	X	—	—	—	—	X	3
Tantilla tritaeniata	—	—	—	X	—	—	—	—	—	1

Table 3. (continued) Distribution of the Herpetofauna in the Habitat Types of the Bay Islands and Cayos Cochinos

Species	Hardwood Forest	Pine Forest	Mangrove Forest	Coconut Groves[1]	Ironshore Formation	Swamps & Marshes	Estuaries	Marine	Urban	Totals
Tretanorhinus nigroluteus	X	—	—	—	—	X	—	—	—	2
Micrurus ruatanus	X	—	—	X	—	—	—	—	—	2
Totals (55)	38	3	10	20	4	11	3	3	10	—

[1]Includes beach margin forest

Table 4. Coefficient of Habitat Resemblance Matrix (CHR = $2C/N_1+N_2$) of Herpetofaunal Relationships For the Habitat Types found in the Bay Islands and the Cayos Cochinos. *N* = species in each habitat type; N = species in common between two habitat types; $\underline{N}$ = Coefficients of Biogeographic Resemblance. Does not include marine habitats.

	Hardwood Forest	Pine Forest	Mangrove Forest	Coconut Groves	Ironshore Formation	Swamps/ Marshes	Estuaries	Urban
Hardwood Forest	38	3	7	14	4	9	0	7
Pine Forest	0.15	3	2	2	1	2	0	2
Mangrove Forest	0.29	0.31	10	5	2	1	1	3
Coconut Groves	0.48	0.17	0.33	20	2	1	0	5
Ironshore Formation	0.19	0.29	0.29	0.17	4	1	0	1
Swamps/Marshes	0.37	0.29	0.10	0.06	0.13	11	0	2
Estuaries	0.00	0.00	0.15	0.00	0.00	0.00	3	0
Urban	0.29	0.33	0.32	0.33	0.15	0.20	0.00	10

do ironshore formations, swamps and marshes, and estuaries.

The herpetofauna of the hardwood forest is most closely related to that of the co-conut groves and vice versa (individual CHR value of 0.48, the highest value in the matrix). The closest resemblances for the other habitat types is as follows: pine forest—urban areas (0.33); mangrove forest—coconut groves (0.33); ironshore formations—pine forest and mangrove forest (0.29); swamps and marshes—hardwood forest (0.37); estuaries—mangrove forest (0.15); urban settings—pine forest and coconut groves (0.33).

Biogeographic Relationships and Significance of the Herpetofauna of the Bay Islands and Cayos Cochinos

Guanaja, Roatán (together with Barbareta), Utila, and the Cayos Cochinos each comprise one of the 38 ecophysiographic areas of Honduras recognized by McCranie and Wilson (2002). The distribution of the 55 species of amphibians and reptiles known from these islands is indicated in Table 2. The numbers of species on each island ranges from a low of 12 on Cayo Cochino Grande to a high of 37 on Isla de Utila.

Duellman's (1990) Coefficient of Biogeographic Resemblance algorithm (see Materials and Methods section for a description of this algorithm) can reveal the degree of resemblance the herpetofaunas of the islands of Islas de la Bahía to one another and to the herpetofauna on the opposite mainland. The Coefficient of Biogeographic Resemblance (CBR) values are indicated in Table 5.

The Cayos Cochinos lie closest to the mainland of Honduras and would be expected to show the greatest resemblance to its herpetofauna, as compared to the herpetofauna of the Bay Islands, and the least amount of endemism. They also are relatively small islands and should possess a relatively small herpetofauna. The last two hypotheses are supportable, but the first is not (Table 5) due to the small number of species found on the Cayos Cochinos.

Table 5. Coefficient of Biogeographic Resemblance Matrix (CBR = 2C/N1+N2) of Herpetofaunal Relationships for the Islands of Islas de la Bahía and the Adjacent Mainland. N = species in each region; N = species in common between two regions; $\underline{N}$ = Coefficients of Biogeographic Resemblance.

	Utila	Roatán	Barbareta	Guanaja	Cayos Cochinos	Mainland
Utila	*37*	20	11	19	13	30
Roatán	<u>0.61</u>	*29*	14	17	11	19
Barbareta	<u>0.43</u>	<u>0.65</u>	*14*	12	9	9
Guanaja	<u>0.61</u>	<u>0.63</u>	<u>0.62</u>	*25*	10	18
Cayos Cochinos	<u>0.46</u>	<u>0.46</u>	<u>0.55</u>	<u>0.45</u>	*19*	15
Mainland	<u>0.41</u>	<u>0.27</u>	<u>0.14</u>	<u>0.26</u>	<u>0.23</u>	*111*

Of the 19 species known from the Cayos Cochinos, all but two (*Phyllodactylus palmeus* and *Anolis allisoni*) occur on the mainland and, in fact, with the exception of *Ctenosaura mela-nosterna* and *Leptotyphlops goudotii*, on the portion of the mainland directly opposite the cays (i.e., the West-central Caribbean Lowlands; see Map 58 in McCranie and Wilson, 2002). In addition, all but five of those 19 species (*Kinosternon leucostomum, Ctenosaura melanosterna, Norops lemurinus, Sphenomorphus cherriei,* and *Leptodeira septentrionalis*) are recorded from one or more of the Bay Islands.

The Bay Islands have a recorded herpetofauna of 50 species. Given their greater distance from the mainland, all major Bay Islands should have less resemblance of its her-petofauna to that of the mainland than do the Cayos Cochinos. However, this is not the case (Table 5) due to the larger numbers of species found on Utila, Roatán, and Guanaja compared to the Cayos Cochinos. Also, the size of the herpetofauna should decrease but exhibit a higher level of endemism the more distant a given island is from the mainland. The number of species known from each of the three major Bay Islands does decrease with great-er distance from the point on the mainland where the submarine ridge upon which these islands lie joins the mainland. Utila, the closest of the three at about 63 km from Tela, has a known herpetofauna of 37 species (67.3% of the total of 55 species for the Islas de la Bahía). Five of the 37 species (13.5%) are endemic to the Islas de la Bahía (*Phyllodactylus palmeus, Sphaerodactylus rosaurae, Ctenosaura bakeri, Norops bicaorum,* and *N. utilensis*); the last three of these are Utila endemics. Roatán is 105 km from Tela (measured from its westernmost point) and possesses a herpetofauna of 29 species, seven of which (24.1% endemism) are endemic to the Islas de la Bahía. Five of these are endemic to Roatán (*Ctenosaura oedirhina, Norops roatanensis, Enulius roatanensis, Oxybelis wilsoni,* and *Micrurus ruatanus*); the other two (*Phyllodactylus palmeus, Sphaerodactylus rosaurae*) are endemic to the Islas de la Bahía. Guanaja is 177 km from Tela and has a herpetofauna of 25 species, three of which (12.0% endemism) are endemic to the Islas de la Bahía (*Phyllodactylus palmeus, Enulius bifoveatus,* and *Tantilla tritaeniata*), with the last two of these endemic to Guanaja. Thus, whereas the number of species on the three major Bay Islands does decrease with greater distance from the mainland, the higher level of endemism the more distant an island is from the mainland is only true in two of the three cases. Guanaja, the most distant island has the lowest ende-mism level (12.0%) of the three islands.

Of the 50 species found on the Bay Islands, 13 (26.0%) do not occur on the mainland of Honduras (*Phyllodactylus palmeus, Sphaerodactylus rosaurae, Ctenosaura bakeri, C. oedirhina, Anolis allisoni, Norops bicaorum, N. roatanensis, N. utilensis, Enulius bifoveatus, E. roatanensis, Oxybelis wilsoni, Tantilla tritaeniata,* and *Micrurus ruatanus*). Of these 13 species, all but two (*A. allisoni* and *Phyllodactylus palmeus*) are endemic to the Bay Islands (22.0% endemism), with *P. palmeus* otherwise occurring only on the Cayos Cochinos. *Anolis allisoni* also occurs on Cuba and on cays and islands off the coast of Belize and Quintana Roo, Mexico.

The relationships of the large majority of the 12 species endemic to the Bay Islands lie with mainland lineages. Only a single endemic (*Sphaerodactylus rosaurae*) is related to an Antillean group of creatures (*S. scaber* group; L. Wilson and Hahn, 1973). The closest rela-tives of the 11 remaining species are as follows:

Phyllodactylus palmeus	*Phyllodactylus insularis* (Dixon, 1968)
Ctenosaura bakeri	*Ctenosaura oedirhina* (Köhler et al., 2000)
Ctenosaura oedirhina	*Ctenosaura bakeri* (Köhler et al., 2000)
Norops bicaorum	*Norops roatanensis* (Köhler and McCranie, 2001)

Norops roatanensis	*Norops bicaorum* (Köhler and McCranie, 2001)
Norops utilensis	*Norops pentaprion* (Köhler, 1996a)
Enulius bifoveatus	*Enulius flavitorques* (McCranie and Köhler, 1999)
Enulius roatanensis	*Enulius flavitorques* (McCranie and Köhler, 1999)
Oxybelis wilsoni	*Oxybelis fulgidus* (Villa and McCranie, 1995)
Tantilla tritaeniata	*Tantilla taeniata* (L. Wilson and McCranie, 1999)
Micrurus ruatanus	*Micrurus nigrocinctus* (Campbell and Lamar, 1989)

Phyllodactylus palmeus and *P. insularis* are sister species, which were both derived from mainland *P. tuberculosus* (Dixon, 1968). The two endemic species of *Ctenosaura* are sister species and are part of a clade containing the mainland taxa *C. melanosterna* (which also occurs on the Cayos Cochinos) and *C. palearis* (Köhler et al., 2000). *Norops bicaorum* and *N. roatanensis* are apparent sister species and both belong to the *lemurinus* species group (Köhler and McCranie, 2001), which also includes the mainland taxa *N. lemurinus, N. serranoi,* and *N. vittigerus* (*N. lemurinus* also occurs on Cayo Cochino Grande). *Norops utilensis* is a member of the *pentaprion* group, which includes an uncertain number of mainland taxa, one of which is *N. pentaprion* (Köhler, 1996a). The two endemic species of *Enulius* both are apparently most closely related to *E. flavitorques* (McCranie and Köhler, 1999), a mainland member of the genus (which also is known from Utila). *Oxybelis wilsoni* is a sister species of *O. fulgidus* (Villa and McCranie, 1995), a mainland member of the genus (which also occurs on Utila). *Tantilla tritaeniata* is apparently most closely related to *T. taeniata* (L. Wilson and McCranie, 1999), a mainland species belonging to the *taeniata* group (L. Wilson, 1999). Finally, *Micrurus ruatanus* is apparently most closely related to the mainland taxon *M. nigrocinctus* (Campbell and Lamar, 1989), which occurs on other islands along the Caribbean coast of Central America, as well as on the mainland.

L. Wilson and Hahn (1973) arranged the herpetofauna of the Bay Islands into three assemblages, based on the knowledge of the distributions of the 35 species then known to occur there. These assemblages are: (1) an endemic assemblage; (2) a West Indian assemblage; and (3) a mainland Honduran assemblage. L. Wilson and Cruz Díaz (1993) utilized the same assemblages, slightly modifying the definition of the endemic assemblage to include a species earlier thought to be restricted to the Bay Islands, but shown by them to also occur on the Cayos Cochinos. Given our inclusion of the marine turtles and the discovery of one introduced species since L. Wilson and Hahn's (1973) and L. Wilson and Cruz Díaz's (1993) work, two additional assemblages are added.

Endemic Assemblage

Phyllodactylus palmeus	*Norops utilensis*
Sphaerodactylus rosaurae	*Enulius bifoveatus*
Ctenosaura bakeri	*Enulius roatanensis*
Ctenosaura oedirhina	*Oxybelis wilsoni*
Norops bicaorum	*Tantilla tritaeniata*
Norops roatanensis	*Micrurus ruatanus*

West Indian Assemblage

Anolis allisoni	*Norops sagrei*

Marine Assemblage

Caretta caretta	*Eretmochelys imbricata*
Chelonia mydas	

Mainland Honduran Assemblage

Hyla microcephala

Scinax staufferi

Smilisca baudinii

Leptodactylus melanonotus

Rana berlandieri

Rana vaillanti

Crocodylus acutus

Trachemys venusta

Kinosternon leucostomum

Coleonyx mitratus

Sphaerodactylus millepunctatus

Thecadactylus rapicauda

Basiliscus vittatus

Ctenosaura melanosterna

Ctenosaura similis

Iguana iguana

Norops lemurinus

Norops sericeus

Mabuya unimarginata

Sphenomorphus cherriei

Gymnophthalmus speciosus

Cnemidophorus lemniscatus

Leptotyphlops goudotii

Boa constrictor

Coniophanes bipunctatus

Coniophanes imperialis

Dryadophis melanolomus

Drymarchon melanurus

Enulius flavitorques

Imantodes cenchoa

Leptodeira septentrionalis

Leptophis mexicanus

Oxybelis aeneus

Oxybelis fulgidus

Pseudelaphe flavirufa

Tretanorhinus nigroluteus

Introduced Assemblage

Bufo marinus

Hemidactylus frenatus

The largest assemblage is the Mainland Honduran Assemblage, with 36 species or 65.5% of the total herpetofauna. The next largest is the Endemic Assemblage, comprising 12 species or 21.8% of the total. The remaining three assemblages contain two, three, and two species, respectively, and collectively make up 12.7% of the total.

The 36 members of the Mainland Honduran Assemblage, as might be expected, are rather widely distributed on the mainland. McCranie (in prep.) uses a set of 13 categories to allocate the reptilian species according to broad patterns of distribution. Nine of these 13 categories contain members of the Mainland Honduran Assemblage. These nine categories can be defined as follows:

A. Northern terminus of the range in the United States (or Canada) and southern terminus in South America;

B. Northern terminus of the range in the United States and southern terminus in Central America south of the Nicaraguan Depression;

C. Northern terminus of the range in the United States and southern terminus in Nuclear Middle America;

D. Northern terminus of the range in Mexico north of the Isthmus of Tehuantepec and southern terminus in South America;

E. Northern terminus of the range in Mexico north of the Isthmus of Tehuantepec and southern terminus in Central America south of the Nicaraguan Depression;

F. Northern terminus of the range in Mexico north of the Isthmus of Tehuantepec and southern terminus in Nuclear Middle America;

G. Northern terminus of the range in Nuclear Middle America and southern terminus in South America;

H. Northern terminus of the range in Nuclear Middle America and southern terminus in Central America south of the Nicaraguan Depression;

J. Endemic to Honduras (including insular endemics);

The 36 members of the Mainland Honduran Assemblage are allocated to these categories as follows:

Category A—*Drymarchon melanurus, Leptodeira septentrionalis,* and *Oxybelis aeneus.*

Category B—*Smilisca baudinii.*

Category C—*Rana berlandieri* and *Coniophanes imperialis.*

Category D—*Hyla microcephala, Leptodactylus melanonotus, Rana vaillanti, Crocodylus acutus, Trachemys venusta, Kinosternon leucostomum, Basiliscus vittatus, Iguana iguana, Mabuya unimarginata, Leptotyphlops goudotii, Boa constrictor, Enulius flavitorques, Imantodes cenchoa, Oxybelis fulgidus,* and *Tretanorhinus nigroluteus.*

Category E—*Scinax staufferi, Norops lemurinus, N. sericeus, Sphenomorphus cherriei, Coniophanes bipunctatus, Dryadophis melanolomus,* and *Leptophis mexicanus.*

Category F—*Pseudelaphe flavirufa.*

Category G—*Thecadactylus rapicauda, Gymnophthalmus speciosus,* and *Cnemidophorus lemniscatus.*

Category H—*Coleonyx mitratus, Sphaerodactylus millepunctatus,* and *Ctenosaura similis.*

Category J—*Ctenosaura melanosterna.*

All but seven of the 36 species fall into categories in which the northern terminus of the range lies in the United States or Mexico north of the Isthmus of Tehuantepec and the southern terminus lies somewhere between Nuclear Middle America and South America. The six species in categories G and H have ranges in which the northern terminus is in Nuclear Middle America and the southern terminus is in Central America south of the Nicaraguan Depression or in South America. Only a single species is endemic to the mainland of Honduras (and also occurs on the Cayos Cochinos).

This discussion indicates that the herpetofauna of the Bay Islands and Cayos Cochinos has considerable significance, especially as it is characterized by a fairly high level of endemism. Of the 55 species making up the herpetofauna, 12 or 21.8% are endemic to these islands. The percentage of endemism compares favorably with that for the country of Honduras as a whole. The known herpetofauna of Honduras consists of 344 species (McCranie, 2004; McCranie and Castañeda, 2004; McCranie and Wilson, 2002; McCranie et al., 2002, 2003a, 2003b, 2005; L. Wilson and McCranie, 2002; L. Wilson et al., 2003), of which 79 are endemics. Thus, the percentage of endemism is 23.0%, close to the figure for the Islas de la Bahía. In addition, the island herpetofauna also contains *Anolis allisoni,* a species not known from the mainland of Honduras. Finally, *Ctenosaura melanosterna* is distributed on the Cayos Cochinos; it is otherwise known only from the middle portion of the Aguan Valley on the mainland of Honduras.

Most of the 12 island endemics are restricted to single islands in the Islas de la Bahía; others occur more broadly. The situation is as follows:

Endemic to Utila
Ctenosaura bakeri
Norops bicaorum
Norops utilensis

Endemic to Roatán
Norops roatanensis
Enulius roatanensis

Oxybelis wilsoni
Micrurus ruatanus

Endemic to Guanaja
Enulius bifoveatus
Tantilla tritaeniata

Endemic to Roatán and Barbareta
Ctenosaura oedirhina

Endemic to Utila, Roatán, and Guanaja
Sphaerodactylus rosaurae

Endemic to the Bay Islands and the Cayos Cochinos
Phyllodactylus palmeus

In summary, a relatively high level of endemism characterizes the herpetofauna of the Islas de la Bahía; furthermore, nine of the 12 endemic species (75.0%) are restricted to single islands. The herpetofauna also contains one species, *Anolis allisoni*, that in Honduras occupies only the Islas de la Bahía. In addition, the Cayos Cochinos is inhabited by one species, *Ctenosaura melanosterna*, otherwise known only from a limited range in the mainland Aguan Valley. The Bay Islands also are known to be visited by three species of globally endangered sea turtles. The remainder of the herpetofauna consists of 38 species with relatively broad distributions on the mainland, one introduced toad, and one introduced gecko. With this information, we can evaluate the conservation status of this herpetofauna and the degree to which the protected areas on the islands can act as refuges. In addition, we also wish to make some predictions about the future for this important herpetofauna.

Conservation Status of the Herpetofauna of the Bay Islands and Cayos Cochinos

Island areas are often centers of endemism and, as such, are of significant interest to conservation biologists, who are interested in protecting biodiversity. Conservation biology is a relatively new, multidisciplinary science that seeks to investigate human impact on species, communities, and ecosytems and to develop practical approaches to preventing the extinction of species and to assure they remain parts of fully functioning ecosystems (Primack, 1998). This science developed in response to the biodiversity crisis, a term used to describe what biologists believe to be the sixth mass extinction episode. A mass extinction episode is a time in geological history when the actual rate of extinction is many hundreds, if not thousands, of times as great as the background extinction rate, the rate at which species normally become extinct. Five such natural mass extinction episodes have occurred in the geological past, at intervals of about 27 million years (Primack, 1998). The best known of these episodes is the one that took place at the close of the Cretaceous period, 65 million years ago, when all the dinosaurs and other large reptiles became extinct, paving the way for the rise of mammals in terrestrial communities. On the other hand, the most dramatic such episode took place about 250 million years ago, at the end of the Permian period, when about half of all animal families, including over 95% of all marine species, as well as many trees, amphibians, most bryozoans and brachiopods, and all trilobites disappeared (Primack, 1998).

Unlike the natural mass extinction episodes of the geological past, the current episode is the work of humans (E. Wilson, 2002). Coincidentally, this episode is occurring at the same time the global diversity of species has reached an all-time high (Primack, 1998). Efforts to assess the extent of the current anthropogenic extinction episode are hampered by our lack of knowledge of most organismal groups, especially those that are less obvious, such as nematode worms, fungi, and bacteria. Primack (1998:152) estimated that "Extinction rates for … 99.9% of the world's species are just rough guesses at present." Nonetheless, estimates of the current extinction rate are as much as 1000 to 10,000 times the background extinction rate (E. Wilson, 2002).

L. Wilson and McCranie (2004) attempted to assess the conservation status of the members of the Honduran herpetofauna (exclusive of the marine species). They devised a means of predicting vulnerability to anthropogenic damage based on three sets of criteria and assigned a composite environmental vulnerability score (EVS) to each member of the herpetofauna known at the time of the submission of that paper. These scores range from 3 to 17 for amphibians and 4 to 19 for reptiles. These ranges were each broken into three categories of low, medium, and high vulnerability. Low vulnerability scores range from 3 to 9 for amphibians and 4 to 9 for reptiles. Medium scores vary from 10 to 13 for amphibians and reptiles and high scores from 14 to 17 for amphibians and 14 to 19 for reptiles.

Application of these categorizations to the non-marine herpetofauna of the Islas de la Bahía is as follows:

Low Vulnerability:

Bufo marinus	*Sphenomorphus cherriei*
Hyla microcephala	*Gymnophthalmus speciosus*
Scinax staufferi	*Leptotyphlops goudotii*
Smilisca baudinii	*Boa constrictor*
Leptodactylus melanonotus	*Dryadophis melanolomus*
Rana berlandieri	*Drymarchon melanurus*
Rana vaillanti	*Enulius flavitorques*
Kinosternon leucostomum	*Imantodes cenchoa*
Sphaerodactylus millepunctatus	*Leptodeira septentrionalis*
Basiliscus vittatus	*Leptophis mexicanus*
Norops lemurinus	*Oxybelis aeneus*
Norops sericeus	*Tretanorhinus nigroluteus*
Mabuya unimarginata	

Medium Vulnerability:

Crocodylus acutus	*Anolis allisoni*
Trachemys venusta	*Norops sagrei*
Coleonyx mitratus	*Cnemidophorus lemniscatus*
Hemidactylus frenatus	*Coniophanes bipunctatus*
Thecadactylus rapicauda	*Coniophanes imperialis*
Ctenosaura similis	*Oxybelis fulgidus*
Iguana iguana	*Pseudelaphe flavirufa*

High Vulnerability:

Phyllodactylus palmeus	*Norops utilensis*
Sphaerodactylus rosaurae	*Enulius bifoveatus*
Ctenosaura bakeri	*Enulius roatanensis*
Ctenosaura melanosterna	*Oxybelis wilsoni*
Ctenosaura oedirhina	*Tantilla tritaeniata*
Norops bicaorum	*Micrurus ruatanus*
Norops roatanensis	

The three sea turtles that visit the Bay Islands are all globally endangered from over-exploitation and would have to be placed in the high vulnerability category as well. Thus, in summary, 25 species or 45.5% of the total fall into the low vulnerability category, 14 or 25.5% into the medium vulnerability category, and 16 or 29.1% into the high vulnerability category. The percentage values differ from those provided by L. Wilson and McCranie (2004) for the entire Honduran non-marine herpetofauna in that a higher percentage of Islas de la Bahía species fall into the low vulnerability category (45.5%, as opposed to 21.6%, respectively) and a lower percentage fall into the medium vulnerability category (25.5%, as opposed to 47.0%, respectively). The percentage figures for the high vulnerability category, however, are similar for the two areas (29.1%, as opposed to 31.4%, respectively). These distinctions are due to the presence of a number of endemic species dispersed among a relatively large number of broadly occurring, ecologically tolerant species on the Islas de la Bahía.

The categorization above represents only an initial step in attempting to determine the conservation status of the Bay Island and Cayos Cochinos herpetofauna. Assessments of the population status of the constituent species need to be undertaken. In addition, an assessment of the degree to which the existing protected areas will provide ostensibly perpetual protection for the members of the herpetofauna is necessary. An initial step in this direction is taken in the following section.

Conservation Efforts on the Bay Islands and Cayos Cochinos

The government of Honduras has established a number of protected areas, a few of which are located on the Bay Islands and Cayos Cochinos. Apparently the first to be established on the islands was the Guanaja Forestry Reserve (Zona Forestal Protegida), founded in 1961 to protect the island's pine forests. However, as discussed by Stonich (2000:111), "in 1992 few residents were aware that these forests had been protected. Moreover, a management plan had never been drafted, personnel had never been assigned, and no research had ever been conducted." This scenario has not changed since 1992. In addition, these forests reportedly were heavily damaged during Hurricane Mitch in 1998. The Port Royal Wildlife Refuge (Refugio de Vida Silvestre) was established in 1979 by the municipality of José Santos Guardiola, Roatán; however, this refuge is beset by the same problems as the Guanaja Reserve (Stonich, 2000).

Three marine reserves (Sandy Bay-West End Marine Reserve on Roatán, Turtle Harbor Reserve on Utila, and Mangrove Bight-North East Bight on Guanaja), designed to protect from the shoreline to the reefs, were established on the Bay Islands. The marine reserve on Guanaja apparently also protects the mangrove forest found there (Anonymous,

No Date). All three of these marine reserves were established by local municipal ordinance and are managed through BICA, the Bay Islands Conservation Association (Stonich, 2000). Stonich (2000:111) described the Sandy Bay-West End Reserve as "the best known and well-funded protected area on the islands." Stonich (2000) then discussed much of the tarnished history of this reserve and concluded (p. 116), "In light of the current economic climate and substantial controversies surrounding the reserve, BICA and its supporters are faced with a formidable challenge" in their efforts to implement management plans for this reserve. Given the marine nature of these three reserves, only the three species of sea turtles known from the Bay Islands (*Caretta caretta*, *Chelonia mydas*, and *Eretmochelys imbricata*) would be afforded any degree of protection in a perfectly managed reserve. The mangrove forests of Guanaja are unknown herpetologically, so we can offer no information on what species may occur there. The same holds true for the pine forests of the Guanaja Forest Reserve.

Anonymous (No Date) also indicated that a proposed wildlife reserve on Isla Barbareta would include the island's hardwood and mangrove forests. This supposedly proposed reserve was not listed by Anonymous (2001), the latest list of the protected areas of Honduras, nor is it presently (March 2004) listed on the COHDEFOR website (www.cohdefor.hn/areas_protegidas/). However, much of the island is privately owned, with one of the owners living there adamantly protecting much of the island from intruders (Grismer et al., 2001; McCranie, pers. observ.). As a result, much of the hardwood forest on Barbareta is in excellent condition (unlike that of the remaining Bay Islands) and the large iguanid lizards *Ctenosaura oedirhina* and *Iguana iguana* are abundant and reach large sizes.

Another protected area on the Cayos Cochinos and the conservation efforts of a German group on Utila are discussed in more detail in the following paragraphs.

Conservation Project Utila Iguana

To preserve *Ctenosaura bakeri* in its natural environment on Utila, Köhler founded the "Conservation Project Utila Iguana" in 1994 in cooperation with the Honduran Nature Conservation Office (AFE-COHDEFOR) and German and international organizations. Since 1997, this project has been a joint project of the Zoological Society Frankfurt (ZGF) and the Senckenberg Nature Research Society (SNG), Frankfurt. The primary goals of the project are to: 1) develop a broad education and information program for the local community, 2) investigate the natural history and reproductive ecology of *C. bakeri*, 3) begin a headstart program, and 4) protect iguana habitat on Utila. In addition, a survey of the herpetofauna of Utila has been initiated that has resulted in several first time records for amphibians and reptiles on the island, as well as the discovery of two undescribed species of endemic anoles (summarized in Köhler 1998b).

With funding from the ZGF, the project's Iguana Research and Breeding Station was constructed and officially put into operation on 25 April 1998. The station makes effective and continuous work possible, serves as a base for scientists and conservationists, and has become an important center for environmental awareness and education on Utila. In 1999, a headstart program was initiated with encouraging results. The strategy is to capture gravid females on nesting beaches and to move them to enclosures equipped for nesting where they can deposit their eggs in a safe environment. When egg laying is complete, the iguanas are released at their sites of capture. Spent females swiftly return to the protection of the mangrove swamps and are of less interest to poachers without their eggs. The strategy can thus improve the likelihood that those particular animals will survive the nesting season and reproduce again the following year. The eggs are then artificially incubated at 28–32°C on vermiculite and half of the hatchlings released into the mangrove swamp, whereas the remainder are raised for 12 months to help surpass the period of maximum vulnerability to predators.

The visitor's center on the ground floor of the station offers an attractive presentation of information about the Swamper or Utila Iguana, as well as other aspects of the Utila flora and fauna, to both Utila residents and tourists. Enlightening the local people to the threats to their unique iguana is vital to the long-term success of the project. The people of Utila must become aware of the fact that this creature will disappear forever unless protective measures are undertaken. This presents a challenge, particularly given that the islanders widely believe that one can bring in replacement iguanas from the mainland if those on the island should die out. Only through continuing education will the local people become convinced that the Utila Iguana exists nowhere else in the world.

Raising environmental awareness in children is of particular importance to the project. Since 1994, Iguana Station personnel have visited the schools of Utila numerous times each year to work with teachers and pupils regarding nature and species conservation on Utila. Integrative tasks have been carried out with the students in addition to slide shows.

Once the Iguana Station opened, groups of schoolchildren could visit and learn about the flora and fauna of Utila and their endangered status through public exhibits. The problem of waste disposal in mangrove swamps on Utila also is being addressed within the framework of the education program.

Given that hunting and habitat destruction still occur, a nature sanctuary will also be needed. Although the activities of the project have been important positive steps, iguana hunting has yet to be significantly reduced. While legislation exists to protect the Utila Iguana, hunters are not actively deterred, so hunting continues. We commonly observed hunters with three to eight adult iguana carcasses in their bags. During the egg laying season, hunters

Ctenosaura bakeri at the Iguana Station.
Photograph by John Binns

"Headstart" holding pens at the Iguana Station.
Photograph by Breck Bartholomew

not only kill gravid females, but also dig through beach sand to find iguana eggs.

Most recently, the Utila Iguana has become threatened by destruction of its habitat. A new large airport has been opened and several new resorts and roads are being built, including a four-track highway from the airport to the town. On the north side of the island where the most important iguana nesting sites are located, beach areas have been "cleaned" by burning and divided into saleable portions. Once the beach areas have been sold, the mangrove swamps will be cleared and filled with coral debris and garbage, similar to past activity on the southern part of the island. Pristine sections of beach are critical for egg laying by females. Without these nesting areas, the Utila Iguana population will quickly decline. Because these iguanas have no other suitable place to lay their eggs, they face inevitable extinction.

If reserve areas of considerable size cannot be established in the face of this development, the future of Utila's natural populations of animals and plants is not promising. Based on our field research, the regions of Iron Bound and eastern Rock Harbour would provide the most suitable core zone for a planned nature sanctuary. This core zone contains rocky coast, coconut groves (including beach margin forest) behind the rocky belt, hardwood forest, and mangrove swamps. In this area, all vertebrate species known to occur on Utila have been recorded (including the three endemic species of lizards; *C. bakeri, Norops bicaorum, N. utilensis*), as well as the three native species of mangroves. In no other location on the island are these four habitats found in such close proximity. A connecting corridor from Iron Bound and Rock Harbour to the Turtle Harbour Reserve (see p. 176) would protect other ecologically valuable and beautiful habitats, including the oldest Red Mangrove forest on the island, the mangrove area with the highest density of epiphytes on the island, and extensive areas of wet savanna. Most of the total area comprising the planned nature sanctuary (all but the beach and beach margin forest) is owned by the community of Utila, and chances are good that protection of this area can be negotiated. On the other hand, all of the beach areas (including beach margin forest along the coast) are privately owned and would need to be purchased to safeguard them from development.

Aside from its ecological and conservation benefits, the creation of a nature sanctuary on Utila would give the island another tourist attraction, if properly managed. Through the use of nature trails and guided tours in protected areas, visitors could be given the opportunity to discover and observe a diversity of unique reptiles and other animals in their natural environment. Most tourism on Utila today is based on diving. By persuading tourists to spend more time on the island, the nature reserve would have a positive economic impact for the Utila community, as well as for Honduras as a whole. Simultaneously, it would significantly enhance the long-term prospects for conservation of the biodiversity of Utila.

Cayos Cochinos Biological Reserve

The Cayos Cochinos Biological Reserve, encompassing the entire island archipelago and its associated coral reefs, was declared a protected area in 1993. The Cayos Cochinos consist of two rock-based islands, Cayo Cochino Grande and Cayo Cochino Pequeño, twelve tiny sand cays, and the fringing coral reefs (Ogden and Ogden, 1998). The large islands support several habitat types, including oak hill forest, mixed hardwood hill forest, back-beach forest, beach margin forest, ironshore habitat, and scattered mangrove forest (Foster, *in* Bermingham et al., 1998). Foster, *in* Bermingham et al. (1998) recorded 160 species of vascular plants from Cayo Cochino Pequeño, based on a four-day survey. Leschen and Wcislo, *in* Bermingham et al. (1998) noted a low insect diversity, based on work in the dry season. Forty-three species of birds were recorded from both islands and cays, based on visual, acoustic, and mist-net work (Seutin, Thorn, and Bermingham, *in* Bermingham et al., 1998). Cruz (*in* Bermingham et al., 1998) summarized the work of L. Wilson and Cruz Díaz (1993), who recorded 15 species of amphibians and reptiles from the two islands (19 species are now known from these islands; see Table 2). Emmons and Werfel (*in* Bermingham et al., 1998) collected six species of mammals and observed two other species on the two islands.

Emmons and Werfel (*in* Bermingham et al., 1998) reported that *Attaleya* palms occur in large, monospecific stands on the ridgetops of Cayo Cochino Grande. They stated (p. 33), "Both Cayos support large populations of agoutis [*Dasyprocta* cf. *punctata*], probably near overpopulation on CCG [=Cayo Cochino Grande]. These animals feed mainly on the nuts of *Attaleya* palms ... . There is local concern that agoutis are causing the rapid spread of *Attalea* [sic], which shades out other tree species and may decrease the plant diversity of the island. This could be the case, because agoutis help propagate palms by burying their seeds. An interesting local rumour holds that agoutis only became numerous when permits were given to collect boas on the island for the pet trade, and 5,000 boas were taken within only two years." Unfortunately, illegal trafficking of wild caught Cayos Cochinos boas continues to the present time (see Remarks for *Boa constrictor*).

An entire issue of *Revista de Biología Tropical* (vol. 46, suppl. 4) was devoted to a survey of the marine and terrestrial flora and fauna of the Cayos Cochinos conducted for 20 months (May 1995 to January 1997), beginning about a year and a half past the time the area was set aside as a biological reserve (Guzmán, 1998).

The Cayos Cochinos Biological Reserve is clearly the most substantially established and best maintained of the relatively few protected areas on the Bay Islands and Cayos Cochinos. In general, however, when compared to the situation on the mainland of Honduras, relatively little attention has been given to the establishment and maintenance of protected areas on the Bay Islands, a factor affecting the prospects for the herpetofauna of the Bay Islands and Cayos Cochinos.

The Future of the Herpetofauna of the Bay Islands and Cayos Cochinos

Assessment of the prospects of the members of the Honduran herpetofauna has been attempted recently in several papers. The first such attempt was that of L. Wilson et al. (2001), which attempted to determine how well the existing system of protected areas offered refuge to the entire herpetofauna known at that time. L. Wilson et al. (2001:152) concluded that "All told, 75.4% of the Honduran herpetofauna is given some measure of protection in the existing system of biotic reserves," and also indicated that "This is a significantly smaller percentage, however, than the 90.9% that would be protected under the system of 25 reserves suggested by [them]."

L. Wilson and McCranie (2004) evaluated the conservation status of the entire Honduran herpetofauna and concluded that the prospects are growing less promising, primarily due to the lack of adequate control of human population growth and the impact of such uncontrolled growth on environmental stability. These authors (2004:31) documented a frightening trend by stating that "It is … evident that we have been idle too long, and that the study of the Honduran herpetofauna has turned a corner into a torturous maze from which there is no easy exit. It is already clear … that a new era has been breached—one in which advances in our cataloguing of the herpetodiversity of Honduras [are] being offset by documented losses of that same diversity over the last decade or so. We are, thus, fighting an uphill battle on very slippery slopes." L. Wilson and McCranie (2004) produced a set of recommendations for the protection of the Honduran herpetofauna, concluding with the following (p. 32): "Our strongest recommendation is that the steps outlined above be taken with all dispatch possible. We have demonstrated that populations of a highly significant number of species of Honduran amphibians and reptiles are already in decline or have disappeared, especially of the most important segment containing the endemic species and those whose distribution is otherwise restricted to Nuclear Middle America. In addition, deforestation has been demonstrated to be increasing at an exponential rate, commensurate with the increase in human population. Deforestation is the principal type of habitat destruction in Honduras, which is, in turn, the major threat to the highly distinctive and important Honduran herpetofauna. There is, in the final analysis, no time to dawdle."

L. Wilson and McCranie (2003) created a process for identifying herpetofaunal indicator species, the biological characteristics of which were used to establish a gauge of environmental stability for most of the ecophysiographic areas existing in Honduras. They pointed again to uncontrolled human population growth as the major culprit in the erosion of the quality of natural environments in Honduras. Their analysis of stability of herpetofaunal populations in the most vulnerable taxa in 26 ecophysiographic areas in the country indicated that 23 of these 26 areas are judged unstable. L. Wilson and McCranie (2003:67) concluded, "The construction of a sustainable human society in Honduras is crucial for the long-term stability of its herpetofauna… Any change will have to occur soon because the

Honduran herpetofauna is being subjected to destructive changes at a rate that threatens to overwhelm all efforts to reverse them."

Given these dire prognostications, the question applies equally well to the prospects for the herpetofauna of the Bay Islands and Cayos Cochinos. Human activity on the Bay Islands presents a somewhat different set of environmental pressures than seen on the mainland, about which two of us (McCranie and Wilson) and our colleague Josiah H. Townsend have written elsewhere (McCranie et al., in prep.). Nonetheless, the major threat to viable, sustainable organismic populations is and will continue to be for the foreseeable future, uncontrolled human population growth (E. Wilson, 2002).

Biologists have demonstrated that, as much as we might like to think otherwise, human beings are as much a product of organic evolution as is any other creature on Earth (Wright, 1994). As such, and even though our cultural evolution has brought us to the point where computer technology has given us the Internet, aerospace technology has allowed us to put people in space, and medical technology has successfully battled age-old scourges, we have not been able to entirely escape our evolutionary past.

One of the holdovers from this past is that our attention is usually directed inwardly to the day-to-day concerns for individual survival. In this self-serving attitude, we are only following the dictates of natural selection, a major force behind organic evolution, which rewards individuals that do the best job of surviving to reproduction. If a raison d`être for life exists, it is reproduction, "perhaps the ultimate adaptive activity of all organisms" (Morgan and Carter, 2002:603). The urge to reproduce is so strong in humans, as with all other organisms, that few of us resist having children.

On the other hand, relatively few humans appear to appreciate the connection between having children themselves and the impact such activity will have on the growth of the human population as a whole. Such a significant intellectual disconnect exists between the one and the other that most of us appear not to be troubled by nor are even aware of our contribution to the exponential growth of the global human population. Evolution has not prepared us to be holistic thinkers.

Beyond all this, exponential population growth is a difficult concept for many to grasp, especially with respect to the way in which population numbers increase in the final stages of such growth, defined by Raven and Berg (2001:G-6) as "The accelerating population growth that occurs when optimal conditions allow a constant rate of increase over a period of time." They further stated (2001:G-6) that "When the increase in population number versus time is plotted on a graph, exponential population growth produces a characteristic J-shaped curve." This J-shaped or exponential growth curve indicates a large increase in population number over a relatively short period of time in the upper portion of the "J" or the final stages of this pattern of growth.

The degree of exponential growth depends on the rate of increase or the growth rate. This rate is the natural increase of a population, expressed as percent per year (Raven and Berg, 2001). The natural increase depends, in turn, on the relationship between the birth rate and the death rate of the population. Based on this relationship and the natural increase this relationship produces, one can calculate the doubling time in years for a population. The formula for doubling time is: D. T. = 70 / % increase. The demographic data for Honduras can be used as an example of how to determine doubling time for a population. The birth rate for Honduras is 33 per sample population of 1000; the death rate is 6 per 1000. The rate of natural increase, thus, is 33–6/1000 x 100 = 2.7%. Inserting this figure into the doubling time formula gives the following: 70/2.7 = 25.9 years. Thus, the time it will take to double the current population size of Honduras of about 8.5 million (estimated from the mid-2001 figure given in Raven and Berg, 2001) to 17.0 million is 25.9 years, *assuming the current trend remains the same over this period of time.* This population figure will be reached in early 2029. In early 2055, the Honduran population should have increased to 34 million. Thus, within about the next half century, the population of Honduras is expected to quadruple! This growth also will increase population density by the same factor.

The calculations indicated in the paragraph above portend extreme, likely insuperable difficulties for Honduras in the coming century, *again* assuming that the current trend of population growth is maintained. The impact that this pattern of uncontrolled human population growth will have on the Islas de la Bahía is reasonably clear, because the beginnings of this trend for the region are already apparent.

For much of their history, the Islas de la Bahía have been relatively lightly populated (Stonich, 2000). The population has been largely confined to the low coastal areas, which, in the case of Roatán and Guanaja, are limited in area (see section on physiography above). This situation is changing relatively rapidly because of two intertwined developments: (1) tourism and (2) influx of transmigrants from the mainland. Demographic data provided by Stonich (2000:98) "… clearly [demonstrate] a significant increase in the rate of growth during the last two decades." When Wilson first visited the Bay Islands in 1967, the population size was approximately 10,000 (estimated from Fig. 4.1 in Stonich, 2000:99). Stonich (2000:98–99) indicated, "Some recent estimates conclude that the resident population on all the islands may be 50,000." Thus, in the span of time since Wilson's first visit 36 years ago, the population is estimated to have increased five-fold!

Roadkill *Ctenosaura oedirhina* being eaten by a *Cathartes aura* on Isla de Roatán. Photograph by Breck Bartholomew

This remarkable surge has been brought about by an increase in the annual growth rate. The following data from Stonich (2000:98) are instructive: "Between the mid-1800s and the early 1960s, the population of the islands grew at about 3.5% per year—about the same annual rate of growth as on the mainland. From 1961 through 1974 the annual population growth rate increased to about 3.6% annually. However, between 1974 and 1988, the annual rate of growth increased substantially to approximately 4.5% and then skyrocketed to at least 5% between 1988 and 1996." Alarmingly, "The annual rate of increase on the Bay Islands is more significant in light of the decreasing overall rate of growth that occurred on the mainland during the same period: from 3.4% between 1970 and 1980, to 3.3% from 1980 to 1990, and finally to 3.1% between 1990 and 1996" (Stonich, 2000:98). In addition, the Bay Islands "… are undergoing a high rate of urbanization. Currently an estimated 81% of the islands' residents live in urban areas while only 15% live in rural areas" (Stonich, 2000:99), which figure "… is almost twice that on the mainland (44%)" (Stonich, 2000:99).

Stonich (2000:141) also points to tourism development as creating "winners, losers, and enhanced social conflict." She concluded, "The consequences of tourism have included increased social differentiation and a growing gap between rich and poor; the assignment of the majority of *ladinos* [i.e., mestizo mainlanders] and islanders to low-status, low-paid, temporary jobs; reduced access for local people to the natural resources on which they depend for their livelihoods; escalating prices for food, manufactured goods, and housing; land speculation and spiraling land costs; increased outside ownership of local resources; and deterioration of the biophysical environment."

As is typical of situations throughout the Third World, "A very high rate of rural to urban migration has characterized Honduras for the last several decades, as a growing number of impoverished rural families have found it increasingly impossible to eke out a living on their meager farm holdings" (Stonich, 2000:99). Amazingly, "Annual rates of population increase on the islands since 1990 are approximately the same as those of mainland urban areas such as San Pedro Sula and Tegucigalpa (4.5%) and far surpass those of rural areas of Honduras (1.8%)" (Stonich, 2000:99). She continues by saying "The equivalent rates of urban growth on the mainland and on the Bay Islands suggest that poor Hondurans on the mainland believe that the economic opportunities on the islands are equal to those in mainland urban centers. Mainlanders also are responding to the lure of high wages, which often are nearly twice the rates paid on the mainland" (Stonich, 2000:99). Thus, as a consequence of the increasing incapability of many poor Hondurans to live on the land, the mainland *ladino* "land rush to the islands" has been created.

Stonich (2000:99) goes on to say, "The accelerated migration of ladinos has shifted the ethnic composition and distribution of human settlements on the islands. According to data from various national censuses of population, the percentage of ladinos on the Bay Islands grew from 7% in 1970, to 12% in 1981, before reaching 16% by 1988." This ethnic shift, understandably, has been mirrored by a linguistic shift. Stonich (2000:120) noted, "Although the Bay Islands usually are classified as part of the 'English-speaking Caribbean,' the percentage of women and men householders who speak Spanish (89%) exceeds those who speak English (66%). Eighty-four percent of islanders who speak Creole and English as their primary language also speak Spanish, while only 33% of Spanish-speaking ladinos also speak English. This is especially so for relatively recent migrants from the mainland—those who have been on the island for 5 years or less." So, the social character of the Bay Islands is changing rapidly as development of tourism draws mainlanders with the false lure of improved wages, seeding the twin problems of overpopulation and social conflict. Stonich

(2000:142) quoted "… an elderly islander woman whose family has lived on the islands since the 1850s," who pointed up to the hills while standing on the beach in front of her family's home, saying, "'In 20 years, that's where we'll all be … some foreigner will own this place.'" On this stage the future of the island herpetofauna will unfold.

We have indicated in a previous section that the herpetofauna of the Islas de la Bahía possesses considerable significance, inasmuch as it is characterized by a relatively high level of endemism, comparable to that of the mainland. Of the 325 species of amphibians and reptiles occurring on the mainland of Honduras, 68 or 20.9% are endemic to that area). Of a total herpetofauna of 55 species on the Islas de la Bahía, 12 are endemic (21.8%); in addition, one non-endemic species (*Anolis allisoni*) does not occur on the Honduran mainland, and another (*Ctenosaura melanosterna*) occurs in only one other limited locality on the mainland.

In the section on conservation status of the herpetofauna of the Islas de la Bahía, we assigned each of the known members to one of three categories of environmental vulnerability, low, medium, and high. As noted above, 25 species belong to the low vulnerability category, 14 into the medium vulnerability category, and 16 into the high vulnerability category. Those species in the high vulnerability category can be expected to face the most significant threats as the factors described above exacerbate. Of these 16 species, three are marine turtles that are threatened worldwide, 12 are island endemics, and one is a species known otherwise from only a single valley on the mainland. As also noted above, ten of the 12 endemics are limited in distribution to single islands, three to Utila, five to Roatán (including Barbareta in the case of one species), and two to Guanaja. One of the other two is known from all three of the major Bay Islands and the other from both the Bay Islands and the Cayos Cochinos. Theoretically, the ability to survive anthropogenic pressure should be less for the endemic species restricted to single islands than more broadly-occurring species. Such restriction also means that more reserves will be necessary to protect the species involved, eschewing the "one size fits all" reserve concept (i.e., trying to maximize the numbers of species protected within the smallest amount of habitat).

At this juncture in time, the most serious anthropogenic pressure on endemic Islas de la Bahía species comes in the form of hunting iguanas for food (Stonich, 2000). On the other hand, tourism development and land speculation is turning habitat for these creatures into overpriced dwelling places for humans, both residents and tourists. This development and the accompanying *ladino* transmigration also are placing pressure on the existing protected areas.

Basiliscus vittatus from Isla de Roatán.
Photograph by Breck Bartholomew

Glossary

We have included in this glossary the technical terms and their definitions that we believe will be unfamiliar to many readers. We have tried to err on the side of inclusiveness rather than exclusiveness so that terms readily familiar to biologists have been included in the event that they are unfamiliar to lay readers. Some terms included here do not appear in the text, but are found in the definitions of terms that appear in the glossary, and may themselves be unfamiliar to some readers. The glossaries in J. Peters (1964) *Dictionary of Herpetology*, Lee's (1996) *The Amphibians and Reptiles of the Yucatán Peninsula*, McCranie and Wilson's (2002) *The Amphibians of Honduras*, and Savage's (2002) *The Amphibians and Reptiles of Costa Rica* were especially helpful in the construction of this glossary.

Algorithm—any systematic method of solving a particular type of problem.

Allopatric populations—two or more populations of a single species separated from one another by a geographical barrier.

Allopatric species—two or more related species separated from one another by a geographical barrier.

Alveolar surface—in turtles, the masticatory or crushing surface of the jaw.

Amniote—a vertebrate animal possessing an amnion, the innermost of four extraembryonic membranes, surrounding the embryo; reptiles, including birds, and mammals are amniotes.

Amniotic egg—the egg type possessed by amniote vertebrates; in reptiles, including birds, and egg-laying mammals, it is a water-retaining, shelled structure.

Anterior—toward the head; may be used in combination with other directional terms (e.g., anterodorsal).

Anterodorsal—a positional term referring to an area near both the head and upper ends of the body.

Anthropogenic—adjective used to describe conditions or circumstances brought about by the action of humans.

Apical pit—in snakes, a small depression or pair of depressions on the dorsal surface of an epidermal scale, near the posterior end.

Arboreal—adjective referring to organisms that live in trees or bushes.

Autotomy—in some lizards, the separation of the tail, usually through intravertebral breakage, followed by tail regeneration.

Axilla—(pl., axillae) the posterior angle formed with the body by the insertion of the forelimb.

Axillary membrane—in anurans, a web of skin extending from the axillary region to the posterior margins of each upper arm.

Axillary pocket—in anole lizards, a scale-less pocket in the skin at the axilla (q.v.).

Azygous scale—an adjective meaning unpaired, refers to median head scale(s) between other scales.

Barbel—in turtles, a thin, fleshy protuberance, usually located on the head (including the region around the mouth) or neck.

Bartlett Trough—see Cayman Trough.

Bilaterally symmetrical—symmetry in which similar anatomical parts are arranged on opposite sides of a median axis dividing the individual into essentially identical halves (dorsal and ventral surfaces).

Biodiversity—a shorthand term for the diversity (species richness) of life characteristic of a particular area.

Biogeography—the scientific study of the distribution of organisms on Earth.

Biphasic life cycle—life cycle typical of amphibians, in which a larva hatches from the egg and later metamorphoses into the adult.

Bonacca Ridge—a 200 km long submarine ridge that forms the southern edge of the Cayman Trough (q.v.). The Bay Islands are located on this ridge.

Brachiopods—a phylum of marine animals with hinged dorsal and ventral shells enclosing a pair of armlike feeding appendages.

Brackish—pertaining to an aquatic habitat in which the water is intermediate in salinity between fresh and salt water.

Bryozoans—a phylum of small marine animals forming branched, mosslike colonies produced by budding.

Carapace—in turtles, the upper portion of the shell.

Casque—in corytophanid lizards, a posterior bony, helmetlike projection of the head.

Caudal—of or pertaining to the tail.

Cayman Trough—a geological term for the fundamental structural unit that separates the North American and Caribbean tectonic plates. The Bay Islands overlie the southern shoulder of the trough.

Cephalic crest—in corytophanid lizards, a flattened, fleshy lobe arising from the posterodorsal portion of the head, more prominent in males than in females.

Cervical scute—(see nuchal scute).

Cladogram—a repeatedly branching, dichotomously structured phylogenetic tree, used to illustrate the evolutionary relationships of a group of organisms, based on the time sequence in which the branches arose.

Cleidoic egg—(see amniotic egg).

Cloaca—the posterior portion of the digestive tract into which empty the tubes of the excretory and reproductive systems.

Cloacal gland—in some turtles and crocodilians, the glands that open into the cloaca and produce a musk.

Cloacal opening—the vent (q.v.).

Cloacal scute—in snakes, the large scale overlying the vent, which may be single or divided (i.e., bisected by an oblique groove). Frequently called the anal plate in the literature.

Cloacal spur—in boid snakes, the external remnant of the hind limb.

Commensal—adjective used to describe the symbiotic relationship in which one species benefits from the association and the other is neither benefited nor harmed.

Coni apicales—in anurans, a thickened, usually blackened, cone-shaped tip, which can be associated with apex of tubercles or not.

Copulatory organ—intromittent organ used for direct transfer of sperm from male to the cloaca (q.v.) of the female.

Cosmopolitan—having a worldwide distribution.

Costal scute—in turtles, one of the several epidermal lamina lying between the vertebral scutes (q.v.) and marginal scutes (q.v.) that cover the ribs in the carapace (q.v.).

Cranial crests—in anurans, raised bony crests or ridges on the top and sides of the head.

Crocodilian—collective common name of the members of the Order Crocodylia.

Cycloid—in lizards, referring to a type of rounded scale.

Dental formula—in crocodiles, a notation for the number of maxillary teeth anterior to the gap into which the fourth tooth of the lower jaw fits plus the number posterior to this point over the number of teeth on the dentary.

Denticulate—in anurans, tiny pointed projections on skin.

Dewlap—in some iguanid and polychrotid lizards, a distensible (in polychrotids) or non-distensible (in some iguanids), laterally compressed midventral fold of skin found in the throat region.

Digital groove—in anurans, the circum-marginal groove above the disc pad (q.v.) forming the disc cover (q.v.).

Disc—in anurans, "refers to the entire expanded structure on the end of the digit" (Savage, 1987:4).

Disc cover—in anurans, "The dorsal area above the pad, which is bounded by the circum-marginal groove anteriorly and to some extent laterally" (Savage, 1987:4).

Disc pad—in anurans, "The specialized ventral (subdigital) area of adhesive epithelium" (Savage, 1987:4).

Distal—away from the origin of an appendage.

Distally—adjectival form of distal.

Distalmost—the most distal of a series of structures located away from the midaxis of the body.

Diurnal—an adjective that refers to an animal that is active chiefly during the daytime.

DNA molecule—the chemical compound that stores information about structure and function of organisms in the form of strings of nitrogenous bases (q.v.).

Dorsal—the upper surface of the body of a bilaterally symmetrical (q.v.) organism.

Dorsal crest scales—in ctenosaurs and iguanas, the series of enlarged, elongate scales along the dorsal midline of the body.

Dorsal scales—the scales covering the dorsum of the body; in snakes, they are arranged in rows extending the length of the body; these rows are counted at one head length past the head, at midbody, and one head length in front of the vent; may be smooth or keeled (i.e., provided with a median ridge).

Dorsolateral—a positional term referring to an area located approximately midway between the dorsum and the lateral region of the body.

Dorsolateral ridges—in some anurans, paired longitudinal folds in the skin on the dorsolateral region of the body.

Dorsum—the dorsal portion of the body.

Ear opening—in some lizards, the external opening of the auditory meatus; used in lieu of tympanum (q.v.), when the tympanum is recessed below the surface of the head.

Ecosystem—in ecological terminology, a community of organisms and the factors of the non-living environment that support it.

Ectothermic—an adjective describing the condition in which body temperature is determined largely by heat sources external to the organism.

Edificarian—an adjective meaning of or pertaining to human habitation; used in reference to an animal that lives around humans and their structures.

Endemic—restricted in distribution to a particular specified area in which that type of organism presumably evolved.

Endemism—the relative amount of species restricted in distribution to a particular area (e.g., a country) compared to the total number of species occupying that same area.

Escarpment—a steep slope or cliff formed by erosion or faulting.

Escutcheon—in some geckos, a shieldlike structure on the venter and sometimes the adjacent undersurfaces of the legs composed of a series of differentiated glandular scales.

Estuary—an inlet or arm of the sea, especially the lower portion of a river where the salty tide meets the freshwater current.

Family—term used for the taxonomic category (q.v.) between order (q.v.) and genus (q.v.).

Fang—a tooth modified for the conduct of venom.

Femoral pore—in some lizards, one of a series of exocrine gland openings on the posteroventral or ventral surface of the thigh.

Finger disc—in anurans, enlarged, adhesive surface on the tip of the finger.

Fossorial—an adjective meaning pertaining to burrowing or digging; used in reference to an animal that lives underground.

Frontal scale—in turtles, lizards, and snakes, the large unpaired scale on the dorsal surface of the head between the orbits.

Frontoparietal scale—in lizards, the scale(s) lying between the frontal (q.v.) and parietal (q.v.) scales.

Generic name—the first of the two names given to each described species.

Genus—(pl., genera) term used for the taxonomic category (q.v.) between family (q.v.) and specific name (q.v.).

Genetic variability—the variation in the information content of the DNA molecule (q.v.) seen in populations of all organisms.

Girdle—one of two sets of bones that connect the limb bones to the vertebral column in vertebrate animals; either pectoral or pelvic.

Gorgetal scales—in some lizards (e.g., species of *Norops*), the scales located on the dewlap (q.v.), which can be differently colored than the skin between these scales.

Granular—in anurans, the skin surface texture having raised granules (or pustules) that may be visible only with the aid of a microscope (= weakly granular); in lizards, used to describe small, rounded, elevated scales.

Gular—pertaining to the ventral surface of the throat or neck.

Gular fold—in some lizards, a transverse fold of skin found in the gular (q.v.) region.

Gular scales—in lizards, the scales found on the ventral surface of the throat.

Gular scute—in turtles, usually the anteriormost scute or pair of scutes on the plastron (q.v.); in some turtles, an intergular scute (q.v.) is present.

Head casque—in corytophanid lizards, refers to a triangular shaped head casque that projects posteriorly past the head.

Head crest—in some iguanian lizards, refers to a laterally compressed lobe of skin (in *Basiliscus*) or enlarged, dorsally projecting scales.

Heliothermic—an adjective that describes ectothermic (q.v.) organisms that rely on solar radiation to elevate the body temperature.

Hemipenes—paired copulatory organs (q.v.) found in squamate reptiles.

Herbivorous—adjective referring to animals that feed on plants.

Herpetofauna—the amphibians and reptiles of a particular area.

Herpetology—the scientific study of amphibians and reptiles.

Heterogeneous—in anoline lizards, referring to the lateral body scales being of dissimilar sizes.

Hexagonal—in lizards, referring to a scale having six angles and six sides.

Holocene Epoch—the current epoch of the Quaternary Period (q.v.), extending from the close of the Pleistocene Epoch (q.v.; see also Recent Epoch).

Homogeneous—in anole lizards, referring to the lateral body scales being of uniform size throughout.

Homologies—similarities attributable to a common origin.

Hypertrophied arm—in anurans, excessive development of a forelimb.

Imbricate—in some lizards and snakes, referring to scales that are overlapping.

Infralabials—see Infralabial scales.

Infralabial scales—in snakes and lizards, the scales lying ventral to the lip line and extending from the mental scale (q.v.) to the oral rictus (q.v.).

Infralingual plicae—in some lizards, referring to having fleshy longitudinal folds on the lower surface of the tongue.

Infrared-sensitive pits—in some snakes, pits or pores in the skin leading to organs that are capable of sensing thermal radiation of wavelengths longer than those of visible light (heat).

Inner metatarsal tubercle—in anurans, the large raised projection on the ventral surface of the foot at the base of Toe I.

Inner tarsal fold—in anurans, a longitudinal fold of the skin located on the inner, or medial, side of the tarsus (q.v.) adjacent to or connecting with the inner metatarsal tubercle (q.v.).

Intercalary scale—in ctenosaurs, the smaller scales lying between the enlarged, spinous whorls on the tail (see also interwhorl).

Intercalary space—in ctenosaurs, the space between the enlarged, spinous whorls of scales occupied by the intercalary or interwhorl (q.v.) scales.

Intergular scute—in turtles, the single epidermal lamina on the plastron (q.v.) lying between the gular scutes (i.e., the small scute on the anterior portion of the plastron).

Internasal scales—in lizards and snakes, one of the usually two or more scales on the top of the head lying between the nasal scales (q.v.).

Interorbital—between the eyes.

Interparietal scale—in some lizards, a scale on the dorsal midline of the head, lying between the parietals (q.v.).

Interwhorl—in ctenosaurs, a ring of smaller scales encircling the tail, alternating with whorls of enlarged, spinous scales (see also intercalary scale).

Isotherm—an imaginary line on a map connecting points on the Earth's surface that have the same mean temperature or the same temperature at a particular time.

Juxtaposed—in some lizards (e.g., *Cnemidophorus lemniscatus*), referring to scales placed side by side.

Keratin—a durable, complex, water-impermeable protein found in vertebrate animals and making up the larger portion of the epidermal scales of reptiles.

Keratinous—composed of keratin (q.v.).

Kinetic—capable of movement, as in the bones of the skull of squamate reptiles.

Labial pits—(see infrared-sensitive pits).

Lamellae—in some lizards, a series of flat, overlapping scales found on the undersurface of the digits (see subdigital lamellae).

Lateral—the portion of the body of a bilaterally symmetrical organism lying to one side or the other of the sagittal plane (q.v.).

Lateral fleshy fringes—in anurans, the fleshy, infolded (at least in preservative) fringes along the lateral margins of the toes distal to the webbing.

Lateral vocal sacs—in anurans, paired vocal sacs that lie behind the angle of the jaws.

Lenca—a group of indigenous people living on the mainland of Honduras.

Lineage—all of the evolutionary descendents of a common ancestor.

Lyre—a stringed instrument of the harp family used as accompaniment by singers and poetry readers.

Lyriform—in the shape of a lyre (q.v.).

Mandible—collective term for the bones of the lower jaw.

Marginal scute—in turtles, one of several epidermal lamina comprising the outermost series on the carapace (q.v.).

Maxillary bone—one of a pair of marginal dermal bones in the skull of amphibians and reptiles.

Maxillary teeth—teeth attached to the maxillary bone, located along each side of the upper jaw.

Maya—a group of indigenous people occupying the Yucatán Peninsula in Mexico, Guatemala, and Belize, as well as western Honduras, who, in pre-Columbian times (A.D. 300–900), lived within a complex civilization.

Mental scale—the scale lying at the anteriormost point of the lower jaw.

Mesoptychial scales—in teiid lizards, the scales in the throat region lying immediately anterior to the gular fold (q.v.).

Metamorph—an immature anuran recently transformed from the larval stage.

Metatarsal tubercle—in anurans, an elevated, thickened protuberance on the skin of the metatarsus (q.v.).

Metatarsus—in anurans, the portion of the foot supported by the metatarsal bones, extending from the heel to the base of the digits.

Microhabitat—within a habitat, a particular zone or region in which a species is found (e.g., the canopy of a rainforest).

Middorsal—a positional term referring to occurrence along the midline of the upper portion of the body.

Middorsal crest—in some iguanian lizards, referring to enlarged, dorsally projecting, serrated scales on the vertebral row of the body or a large, flat fold of dorsally directed skin.

Modal—pertaining to the number or value that occurs most frequently in a particular series.

Monophyletic—referring to a taxon (q.v.) whose members were derived from a single ancestral species.

Monophyly—condition of having arisen from a single ancestral species.

Nasal scale—one of the series of scales, or the single scale, surrounding the nostril.

Nicaraguan Depression—the low-lying area in Nicaragua between the mountains of Nuclear Middle America (q.v.) and those of lower Central America.

Nitrogenous base—one of four chemical components of the DNA molecule (q.v.) that allow for the storage of information about structure and function.

Nocturnal—an adjective referring to an animal that is active chiefly at night.

Nuchal—referring to the dorsal surface of the neck or neck region.

Nuchal collar—in snakes, a pale colored band on the posterior portion of the head and neck region.

Nuchal crest—in some iguanian lizards, referring to enlarged, dorsally projecting scales on the vertebral row (dorsal midline) on the neck or nuchal region.

Nuchal scute—in turtles, the epidermal plate located at the anteriormost point of the carapace (q.v.).

Nuclear Middle America—the largely mountainous area between the Isthmus of Tehuantepec and the Nicaraguan Depression (q.v.).

Occipital—adjective used in reference to the posterior portion of the head.

Occiput—the posterior portion of the head.

Ocellate—patterned with ocelli (q.v.).

Ocellus—(pl., ocelli) an eyelike structure or pattern element.

Ocular groove—the groove around the eye, separating it from the circumorbital scales.

Ocular scale—in leptotyphlopid snakes, the enlarged head scale overlying the vestigial eye.

Oral rictus—the point of the mouth where the upper and lower jaws form the corner.

Order—in taxonomy, a taxonomic level between class and family (e.g., the Order Anura).

Ornithology—the scientific study of birds.

Organismic—the adjectival form of the word "organism."

Osteoderm—in reptiles, a bony deposit in the form of a plate or scale found in the dermal skin layers.

Outer metatarsal tubercle—in anurans, a small raised projection on the ventral surface of the foot at the base of Toes IV or V.

Oviparous—reproduction by laying of eggs.

Pantropical—in reference to distribution, occurrence in tropical regions around the world.

Para-cloacal tubercles—in coral snakes, protuberances on the surface of the lateral scales of the dorsum in the region of the vent (q.v.).

Paraphyletic—referring to a taxon (q.v.) that excludes some members that share a common ancestor with other members included in the taxon.

Parietal scale—in squamate reptiles, either of a pair or more of enlarged scales on the dorsum of the head, lying immediately posterior to the frontal scale (q.v.) in snakes and lying posterior to the frontoparietal scale(s) (q.v.) in lizards.

Parotoid gland—in anurans, the enlarged, swollen concentration of granular glands located on the head posterior to the eye above the level of the tympanum (q.v.).

Paya—a group of indigenous people currently living on the north coast of Honduras and thought by some archaeologists to have been the original inhabitants of the Bay Islands.

Pech—a group of indigenous people currently living on the north coast of Honduras and thought by some archaeologists to have been the original inhabitants of the Bay Islands.

Pectoral girdle—the bony or cartilaginous structures to which the forelimbs of a vertebrate animal are attached.

Pendulous—suspended so as to swing freely.

Pelvic girdle—the bony or cartilaginous structures to which the hind limbs of a vertebrate animal are attached.

Pentagonal—in lizards, referring to a scale having five angles and five sides.

Pilose—in geckos, referring to the condition of having many hairlike extensions located on the toe pads.

Phalanges—the bones distal to the metacarpals in the fingers or metatarsals in the toes.

Plastral scute—in turtles, any of the epidermal plates covering the plastron (q.v.).

Plastron—in turtles, the lower portion of the shell.

Pleistocene Epoch—the epoch of the Quaternary period (q.v.) prior to the Recent Epoch (q.v.) beginning about 1.8 million years before the present; geological time period when the ice ages occurred and humans appeared.

Plesiomorphic—an ancestral feature or character.

Pleural scute—(see costal scute).

Polyphyletic—referring to a taxon (q.v.) whose members were derived from more than one ancestral form.

Polytypic species—a species of organism composed of two or more distinct subgroups.

Postcloacal scale—in some lizards, one of a pair of enlarged scales lying immediately posterior to the vent (q.v.).

Posterior—away from the head; may be used in combination with other directional terms (e.g., posterolateral).

Postmental scale—in lizards and some snakes, the scale(s) bordering the mental (q.v.) between the first pair of infralabial scales (q.v.).

Postnasal scale—the scale lying immediately posterior to the nostril, divided from the nasal scale (q.v.) in some snakes.

Postoccipital—occupying a position behind the occiput (q.v.).

Postorbital—adjective referring to the region behind the eye.

Precloacal plate—in some lizards, an enlarged scale lying immediately anterior to the cloaca (q.v.).

Precloacal pores—in lizards, openings of exocrine glands situated in the region immediately anterior to the cloaca (q.v.).

Precloacal spur—in teiid lizards of the genus *Cnemidophorus*, a laterally projecting scale extension located anterior to the cloaca (q.v.).

Prefrontal scale—in turtles, lizards, and snakes, one of a pair (or more) of epidermal scutes lying anterior to the frontal scale (q.v.) on the dorsal surface of the head.

Premaxillary teeth—teeth attached to the premaxillary bone, located in the anteromedial portion of the upper jaw.

Proteroglyph dentition—in elapid snakes, a type of dentition in which the relatively rigid (non folding) hollow fangs are located in the anterior portion of the oral cavity.

Quaternary Period—the most recent geological period, consisting of the Pleistocene (q.v.) and Recent (q.v.) Epochs, beginning about 1.8 million years before the present.

Quadruped—a four limbed vertebrate.

Recent Epoch—the most recent geological epoch, beginning about 10,000 years before the present; historical time (see also Holocene Epoch).

Regenerated—in lizards, referring to a lost portion of a tail that has been replaced by a new growth of tissue.

Rostral scale—the scale in snakes and lizard at the anteriormost portion of the snout, lying just above the lip line.

Sagittal plane—the imaginary plane of section that passes from the dorsal midline to the ventral midline of the body of a bilaterally symmetrical organism.

Scientific name—the two-part formal name (generic and specific epithets) given to an organism, which is used to insure accuracy of communication among biologists.

Secondary palate—in crocodilians, the platform of bones roofing the mouth cavity that forms the floor of the nasal passages, the roof of which constitutes the primary palate.

Setae—in gekkonid lizards, the microscopic hairlike structures lying on the surface of the lamellae (q.v.).

Sexual dimorphism—differences in phenotypic structure related to gender.

Shank—used in reference to the hind limb segment between the knee and the heel.

Shank length—length of shank (q.v.), measured from the outer end of the knee to the outer end of the heel.

Species—a group of organisms reproductively isolated from other such groups (biological definition) or a group of organisms occupying a distinct evolutionary trajectory (evolutionary definition).

Specific name—the second of the two names given to each organismic species recognized.

Subarticular tubercles—in anurans, the enlarged raised projections below the articulations of the phalanges (q.v.).

Subcaudal scales—the scales lying on the underside of the tail; may be divided or single.

Subdigital lamellae—the series of overlapping, flat scales on the undersurface of some lizards (e.g., anoles and some geckos; see lamellae).

Subdigital toe pad—in lizards, the dilated ventral portion of the digit, composed of a series of lamellae (q.v.).

Subequal—more or less equal, as in size.

Subgular vocal sac—in anurans, a vocal sac lying in the gular or throat region.

Subocular scales—in lizards and some snakes, the enlarged scales lying below the orbit (q.v.), forming its ventral border.

Subterminal disc pad—in anurans, a thick, fleshy area on the ventral surface of the tip of the digit (also see disc pad).

Sulcus—in lizards, a shallow groove that is generally open on one side.

Supernumerary tubercle—in anurans, the small, raised projections on the ventral surfaces of the digits (associated with the phalanges [q.v.] only), exclusive of the larger subarticular tubercles (q.v.), not to be confused with the tubercles on the fleshy part of the palm or soles called supernumerary palmar tubercles and supernumerary plantar tubercles, respectively, by Lynch and Duellman (1980), or supernumerary (palmar) tubercles and supernumerary plantar tubercles, respectively, by Lynch and Duellman (1997).

Supralabial scales—the scales on the head of a snake or lizard that lie above the lip line and extend from the rostral scale (q.v.) to the oral rictus (q.v.).

Supralabials—(see supralabial scales).

Supranasal scale—(see internasal scales).

Supraocular scales—in lizards and snakes, the enlarged scale or scales lying above the eyes.

Supraorbital semicircles—in anoline lizards, a group of enlarged scales on the dorsal surface of the head arranged in a semicircular pattern bordering the inner portion of the supraocular scales (q.v.).

Supratympanic—position above the tympanum (q.v.).

SVL—abbreviation for snout-vent length, the length from the tip of the snout to the vent (q.v.).

Synapomorphy—a shared derived character, i.e., evolutionary homologies (q.v.) that evolved in an ancestor common to all species on one branch in a cladogram (q.v.), but not common to species on other branches of the same cladogram.

Synonymy—the list of scientific names used by different authors in history to designate the same taxon of organisms; in biological nomenclature, a given taxon (q.v.) at the species level can only have one current scientific name.

Tarsus—in anurans, the hind limb segment between the tibiofibula (q.v.) and metatarsus (q.v.).

Taxon—(pl., taxa) a named taxonomic unit of organisms at any given level of the taxonomic hierarchy (q.v.).

Taxonomic hierarchy—the nested set of categories used to classify organisms (e.g., species, genus, family, etc.).

Temporal—referring to the region on the side of the head lying posterior to the eye.

Terminal—an anatomical position pertaining to the distal (q.v.) end of a structure.

Terrestrial—adjective referring to organisms that live on the ground.

Thumb pad—in anurans, the thick, fleshy or cushiony area on the thumb.

Tibiofibula—in anurans, the compound bone in the lower hind limb between the knee and the heel.

TL—abbreviation for total length, the length from the tip of the snout to the tip of the tail.

Toe disc—in anurans, enlarged, adhesive surface on the tip of the toe.

Tricarinate—having three keels.

Trilobites—a subphylum of extinct arthropods, with a body divided into three lobes, extant from the Cambrian to Carboniferous Periods, about 290 to 570 million years ago.

Tubercle—a rounded, raised projection on the skin.

Tympanum—the rounded or oval shaped, flat membrane covering the external opening of the middle ear and, in anurans, its raised rim (tympanic annulus) as well.

Unicarinate—having a single keel.

Vent—the external opening of the cloaca (q.v.) (also see cloacal opening).

Ventral—the lower surface of the body of a bilaterally symmetrical (q.v.) organism.

Ventral scales—in snakes and lizards, the scales lying on the underside of the body; in most snakes they lie in a single row from the neck to the vent.

Ventrolateral—referring to a position approximately midway between the bottom and lateral portion of an organism.

Vertebral scutes—in turtles, any of a series of unpaired epidermal lamina lying along the dorsal midline of the carapace (q.v.).

Vocal sac(s)—in male anurans, the inflatable pouch(es) in the throat or on the sides of the neck.

Vocal slits—in male anurans, the paired openings in the floor of the mouth leading to the vocal sac(s) (q.v.).

Vomerine teeth—the teeth attached to the vomer bone in the roof of the mouth.

Voucher specimen—a preserved biological specimen used to document distributional and other information.

Webbing—in anurans, the fleshy membrane connecting adjacent digits.

Webbing formula—in anurans, Roman numerals represent fingers or toes and Arabic numerals represent the number of segments of the digits completely or partially free of webbing. 0 indicates the webbing extends to the tip of the digit, 1 indicates the entire terminal segment is free of webbing. A + sign indicates the webbing reaches the proximal end of a subarticular tubercle (q.v.) and a - sign means the webbing reaches the distal end of a subarticular tubercle (q.v.).

Whorl—in ctenosaurs, a ring of enlarged, spinous scales encircling the tail.

Wisconsin glacial period—one of the ice ages that occurred during the Pleistocene Epoch (q.v.).

Literature Cited

Anonymous. No Date. Mapa de Áreas Protegidas de Honduras. Instituto Hondureña de Turismo, Tegucigalpa.

_____. 2001. Estudio sobre Diversidad Biológica de la República de Honduras. Dirección General de Biodiversidad, Secretaría de Recursos Naturales y Ambiente, Tegucigalpa. xi + 158 pp.

Austin, C. C. 2000. Molecular phylogeny and historical biogeography of Pacific Island boas (*Candoia*). Copeia 2000(2):341–352.

Baird, S. F. 1859. Reptiles of the boundary, with notes by the naturalists of the survey, pp. 1–35. *In* W. H. Emory. United States and Mexican Boundary Survey, Part II, Zoology of the Boundary. Dept. Interior, Washington.

Barbour, T. 1928. Reptiles from the Bay Islands. Proc. New England Zoöl. Club 10:55–61.

Bermingham, E., A. Coates, G. Cruz D., L. Emmons, R. B. Foster, R. Leschen, G. Seutin, S. Thorn, W. Wcislo, and B. Werfel. 1998. Geology and terrestrial flora and fauna of Cayos Cochinos, Honduras. Rev. Biol. Trop. 46(Suppl. 4):15–37.

Berry, J. F., and J. B. Iverson. 2001. *Kinosternon leucostomum*. Cat. Amer. Amphib. Reptiles 724.1–724.8.

Brocchi, P. 1877. Sur quelques batraciens raniformes et bufoniformes de l'Amérique Centrale. Bull. Soc. Philomath. Paris, ser. 7, 1:175–197.

Buckley, L. J., and R. W. Axtell. 1997. Evidence for the specific status of the Honduran lizards formerly referred to *Ctenosaura palearis* (Reptilia: Squamata: Iguanidae). Copeia 1997(1):138–150.

Campbell, J. A., and W. W. Lamar. 1989. The Venomous Reptiles of Latin America. Comstock. Publ. Assoc., Ithaca, New York. xii + 425 pp.

Cope, E. D. 1861. Notes and descriptions of anoles. Proc. Acad. Nat. Sci. Philadelphia 13:208–215.

_____. "1861" (1862a). Contributions to the ophiology of Lower California, Mexico and Central America. Proc. Acad. Nat. Sci. Philadelphia 13:292–306.

_____. 1862b. Contributions to neotropical saurology. Proc. Acad. Nat. Sci. Philadelphia 14:176–188.

_____. 1865. Third contribution to the herpetology of tropical America. Proc. Acad. Nat. Sci. Philadelphia 17:185–198.

_____. "1866" (1867). Fifth contribution to the herpetology of tropical America. Proc. Acad. Nat. Sci. Philadelphia 18:317–323.

_____. 1868. An examination of the Reptilia and Batrachia obtained by the Orton Expedition to Equador and the upper Amazon, with notes on other species. Proc. Acad. Nat. Sci. Philadelphia 20:96–140.

_____. "1868" (1869). Sixth contribution to the herpetology of tropical America. Proc. Acad. Nat. Sci. Philadelphia 20:305–313.

_____. "1885" (1886). Thirteenth contribution to the herpetology of tropical America. Proc. Amer. Philos. Soc. 23:271–287.

_____. 1893. Second addition to the knowledge of the Batrachia and Reptilia of Costa Rica. Proc. Amer. Philos. Soc. 31:333–347 (separates published in 1893, in advance of volume published in 1894).

Cuvier, G. 1807. Sur les différentes espèces de crocodiles vivans et sur leurs caractères distinctifs. Ann. Mus. Hist. Natl., Paris 10:8–66.

Daudin, F. M. 1803. Histoire Naturelle, Générale et Particulière des Reptiles; Ouvrage faisant suite aux Ouvres de Leclerc de Buffon, et partie du Cours complet d'Histoire naturelle rédigé par C. S. Sonnini, membre de plusieurs Sociétés savantes. Tome Sixième. F. Dufart, Paris. 447 pp.

David, P., and I. Ineich. 1999. Les serpents venimeux du monde: systématique et répartition. Dumerilia 3:3–499.

Davidson, W. V. 1974. Historical geography of the Bay Islands, Honduras. Southern Univ. Press, Birmingham, Alabama. xvi + 199 pp.

de Queiroz, K. 1987. A new spiny-tailed iguana from Honduras, with comments on relationships within *Ctenosaura* (Squamata: Iguania). Copeia 1987(4):892–902.

Dixon, J. R. 1968. A new species of gecko (Sauria: Gekkonidae) from the Bay Islands, Honduras. Proc. Biol. Soc. Washington 81:419–426.

Dodd, C. K., Jr. 1990. *Caretta caretta*. Cat. Amer. Amphib. Reptiles 483:1–7.

Dubois, A. 1999. Miscellanea nomenclatorica batrachologica. 19. Notes on the nomenclature of Ranidae and related groups. Alytes 17(1–2):81–100.

Duellman, W. E. 1990. Herpetofaunas in Neotropical rainforests: Comparative composition, history, and resource use, pp. 455–505. *In* A. H. Gentry (ed.). Four Neotropical Rainforests. Yale Univ. Press, New Haven. xiii + 627 pp.

_____. 2001. The hylid frogs of Middle America. Soc. Study Amphib. Reptiles, Contrib. Herpetol. 18:i–xvi, 1–694, i–x, 695–1159.

_____. 2003. An overview of anuran phylogeny, classification and reproductive modes, pp. 1–18. *In* B. G. M. Jamieson (ed.). Reproductive Biology and Phylogeny of Anura. Science Publ., Inc., Enfield. vii + 452 pp.

Duméril, A. H. A., M. F. Bocourt, and F. Mocquard. 1870–1909. Études sur les Reptiles. Mission Scientifique au Mexique et dans l'Amérique Centrale. Recherches Zoologiques pour servir a l'Histoire de la Fauna de l'Amérique Centrale et du Mexique. Troisieme Partie.—1re Section. Imprimeire Nationale, Paris. xiv + 1012 pp.

Duméril, A. M. C., and G. Bibron. 1836. Erpétologie Générale ou Histoire Naturelle Complète des Reptiles, Tome Troisième. Contenant l'Histoire de Toutes les Espèces des Quatre Premières Familles de l'Ordre des Lézards ou Sauriens, Savoir: les Crocodiles, les Caméléons, les Geckos et les Varans. Libr. Encyclopédique Roret, Paris. iv + 517 pp.

_____, and _____. 1837. Erpétologie Générale ou Histoire Naturelle Complète des Reptiles. Tome Quatrième. Contenant l'Histoire de Quarante-Six Genres et de Cent Quarante-Six Espèces de la Famille des Iguaniens, de l'Ordre des Sauriens. Libr. Encyclopédique Roret, Paris. ii + 571 pp.

_____, and _____. 1841. Erpétologie Générale ou Histoire Naturelle Complète des Reptiles. Tome Huitième. Comprenant l'Histoire Genéralé des Batraciens, et la Description des Cinquante-Deux Genres et des Cent Soixante-Trois

Espécies des Deux Premiers Sous-Ordres; les Péromèles qui n'ont pas de Membres, et les Anoures qui sont Privés de la Queue. Libr. Encyclopédique Roret, Paris. iii + 792 pp.

_____, and _____. 1844. Erpétologie Générale ou Histoire Naturelle Complète des Reptiles. Tome Sixième. Comprenant l'Histoire Génerale des Ophidiens, la Description des Genres et des Espèces de Serpents non Venimeux, Savoir: la Totalité des Vermiformes ou des Scolécophides, et partie des Cicuriformes ou Azémiophides; en Tout Vingt-Cinq Genres et Soixante-Cinq Espécies. Libr. Encyclopédique Roret, Paris. xii + 609 pp.

_____, _____, and A. H. A. Duméril. 1854. Erpétologie Générale ou Histoire Naturelle Complète des Reptiles. Tome Septième.—Première Partie. Comprenant l'Histoire Naturelle des Serpents non Venimeux. Libr. Encyclopédique Roret, Paris. vii + 1–780 pp.

_____, and A. H. A. Duméril. 1851. Catalogue Méthodique de la Collection des Reptiles du Muséum d'Histoire Naturelle de Paris. Gide et Baudry, Paris. iv + 224 pp.

Ernst, C. H., and R. W. Barbour. 1989. Turtles of the World. Smithsonian Inst. Press, Washington. xii + 313 pp.

_____, F. D. Ross, and C. A. Ross. 1999. *Crocodylus acutus*. Cat. Amer. Amphib. Reptiles 700:1–17.

Frost, D. R., and R. Etheridge. 1989. A phylogenetic analysis and taxonomy of iguanian lizards (Reptilia: Squamata). Univ. Kansas Mus. Nat. Hist., Misc. Publ. 81:1–65.

_____, _____, D. Janies, and T. A. Titus. 2001. Total evidence, sequence alignment, evolution of polychrotid lizards, and a reclassification of the Iguania (Squamata: Iguania). Amer. Mus. Novitates 3343:1–38.

Gray, J. E. 1831. A synopsis of the species of the class Reptilia, pp. 1–110. *In* E. Griffith and E. Pidgeon. The Class Reptilia Arranged by the Baron Cuvier, with Specific Descriptions. Whittaker, Treacher, and Co., London. 481 +110 pp.

_____. 1855. Catalogue of Shield Reptiles in the Collection of the British Museum. Part I. Testudinata (Tortoises). Printed by Order of the Trustees, British Museum (Natural History), London. iv + 79 + ii pp.

Grismer, L. L. 1988. Phylogeny, taxonomy, classification, and biogeography of Eublepharid geckos, pp. 369–469. *In* R. Estes and G. Pregill (eds). Phylogenetic Relationships of the Lizard Families. Essays Commemorating Charles L. Camp. Stanford Univ. Press, Stanford. xi + 631 pp.

_____, L. L. Grismer, K. M. Marson, A. B. Matteson, E. J. R. Sihotang, K. M. Crane, J. Dayov, T. A. Mayer, A.-L. Simpson, and H. Kaiser. 2001. New herpetological records for the Islas de la Bahía, Honduras. Herpetol. Rev. 32(2):134–135.

Günther, A. 1858. Catalogue of Colubrine Snakes in the Collection of the British Museum. Printed by Order of the Trustees of British Museum, London. xvi + 281 pp.

_____. 1885–1902. Reptilia and Batrachia. *In* O. Salvin and F. D. Godman (eds.). Biologia Centrali-Americana; or, Contributions to the Knowledge of the Fauna and Flora of Mexico and Central America. R. H. Porter and Dulau & Co., London. xx + 326 pp.

Gutsche, A. 2003. Geographic distribution. *Enulius flavitorques*. Herpetol. Rev. 34(3):265.

_____, J. R. McCranie, and K. E. Nicholson. 2004. Field observations on a nesting site of *Norops utilensis* Köhler, 1996 (Reptilia, Squamata) with comments about its conservation status. Salamandra 40(3/4):297–302.

Guzmán, H. M. (ed.). 1998. Marine-Terrestrial Flora and Fauna of Cayos Cochinos Archipelago, Honduras. Rev. Biol. Trop. 46(suppl. 4):1–200.

Hallowell, E. "1856" (1857). Notes on the reptiles in the collection of the Academy of Natural Sciences of Philad'a. Proc. Acad. Nat. Sci. Philadelphia 8:221–238.

_____. "1860" (1861). Report upon the Reptilia of the North Pacific Exploring Expedition, under command of Capt. John Rogers [sic], U.S.N. Proc. Acad. Nat. Sci. Philadelphia 12:480–510.

Heyer, W. R. 1970. Studies on the frogs of the genus *Leptodactylus* (Amphibia: Leptodactylidae). VI. Biosystematics of the *melanonotus* group. Los Angeles Co. Mus. Nat. Hist., Contr. Sci. 191:1–48.

_____, A. S. Rand, C. A. G. da Cruz, O. L. Peixoto, and C. E. Nelson. 1990. Frogs of Boracéia. Arq. Zool., Mus. Zool., Univ. São Paulo 31(4):231–410, + audiotape.

Hillis, D. M., and R. de Sá. 1988. Phylogeny and taxonomy of the *Rana palmipes* group (Salientia: Ranidae). Herpetol. Monogr. 2:1–26.

Holdridge, L. R. 1967. Life Zone Ecology. Revised Edition. Trop. Sci. Center, San José, Costa Rica. 206 pp.

Houttuyn, M. 1782. Het onderscheid der Salamanderen van de Haagdissen in 't algemeen, en van de Gekkoos in 't byzonder aangetoond. Verh. Zeeuwsch Gen. Wet. Vlissingen (1)9(2):305–336.

Humphrey, C. 2000. Moon Handbooks: Honduras. Including the Bay Islands and Copán. Second edition. Avalon Travel Publ., Inc., Emeryville, California. 402 pp.

Kaiser, H., C. Cole, A. B. Matteson, T. A. Mayer, A-L. Simpson, J. D. Wray, and L. L. Grismer. 2001a. Natural history notes. *Ctenosaura oedirhina*. Herpetol. Rev. 32(4):253–254.

_____, J. R. Sihotang, K. M. Marson, K. M. Crane, J. Dayov, and L. L. Grismer. 2001b. A breeding population of American crocodiles, *Crocodylus acutus*, on Roatán, Islas de la Bahía, Honduras. Herpetol. Rev. 32(3):164–165.

Kizirian, D. A., and C. J. Cole. 1999. Origin of the unisexual lizard *Gymnophthalmus underwoodi* (Gymnophthalmidae) inferred from mitochondrial DNA nucleotide sequences. Molec. Phylog. Evol. 11(3):394–400.

Kluge, A. G. 1987. Cladistic relationships in the Gekkonoidea (Squamata, Sauria). Misc. Publ. Mus. Zool., Univ. Michigan 173:i–iv, 1–54.

Köhler, G. 1995. Freilanduntersuchungen zur Morphologie und Ökologie von *Ctenosaura bakeri* und *C. oedirhina* auf den Islas de la Bahia, Honduras, mit Bemerkungen zur Schutzproblematik. Salamandra 31(2):93–106.

_____. 1996a. A new species of anole of the *Norops pentaprion* group from Isla de Utila, Honduras (Reptilia: Sauria: Iguanidae). Senckenberg. Biol. 75(1/2):23–31.

_____. 1996b. Additions to the known herpetofauna of Isla de Utila (Islas de la Bahia, Honduras) with the description of a new species of the genus *Norops* (Reptilia: Sauria: Iguanidae). Senckenberg. Biol. 76(1/2):19–28.

_____. 1998a. Further additions to the known herpetofauna of Isla de Utila (Islas de la Bahia, Honduras) with notes on other species and a key to the amphibians and reptiles of the island (Amphibia, Reptilia). Senckenberg. Biol. 77(2):139–145.

_____. 1998b. Herpetologische Beobachtungen in Honduras. I. Die Islas de la Bahía. Natur und Mus. 128(11):372–383.

_____. 2001. Geographic distribution. *Hemidactylus frenatus*. Herpetol. Rev. 32(1):57.

_____. 2003. The Reptiles of Central America. Herpeton Verlag Elke Köhler, Offenbach, Germany. 367 pp.

_____, and J. R. McCranie. 2001. Two new species of anoles from northern Honduras (Reptilia, Squamata, Polychrotidae). Senckenberg. Biol. 81(1/2):235–245.

_____, W. Schroth, and B. Streit. 2000. Systematics of the *Ctenosaura* group of lizards (Reptilia: Sauria: Iguanidae). Amphibia-Reptilia 21(2):177–191.

Lee, J. C. 1996. The Amphibians and Reptiles of the Yucatán Peninsula. Comstock Publ. Assoc., Ithaca, New York. xii + 500 pp.

Liner, E. A. 1994. Scientific and common names for the amphibians and reptiles of Mexico in English and Spanish. Nombres científicos y comunes en Ingles y Español de los Anfibios y los Reptiles de México. Soc. Study Amphib. Reptiles, Herpetol. Cir. 23: i–v, 1–113.

Linnaeus, C. 1758. Systema Naturae per Regna Tria Naturae, Secundum Classes, Ordines, Genera, Species, cum Characteribus, Differentiis, Synonymis, Locis. Tomus I. Editio Decima, Reformata. Laurentii Salvii, Stockholm. 823 pp.

_____. 1766. Systema Naturae per Regna Tria Naturae, Secundum Classes, Ordines, Genera, Species, cum Characteribus, Differentiis, Synonymis. Locis. Tomus I. Editio Duodecima, Reformata. Laurentii Salvii, Stockholm. 532 pp.

Lundberg, M. 2000. Herpetofaunan på Isla de Utila, Honduras. Snoken 30(4):2–8.

_____. 2002. Herpetofaunan på Hog Islands, Honduras. Snoken 32(1):4–13.

Lynch, J. D., and W. E. Duellman. 1980. The *Eleutherodactylus* of the Amazonian slopes of the Ecuadorian Andes (Anura: Leptodactylidae). Misc. Publ., Univ. Kansas Mus. Nat. Hist. 69:1–86.

_____, and _____. 1997. Frogs of the genus *Eleutherodactylus* (Leptodactylidae) in western Ecuador: systematics, ecology, and biogeography. Univ. Kansas Nat. Hist. Mus. Spec. Publ. 23:i–iv, 1–236.

Malone, C. L., and S. K. Davis. 2004. Genetic contributions to Caribbean iguana conservation, pp. 45–57. *In* A. C. Alberts, R. L. Carter, W. K. Hayes, and E. P. Martins (eds.). Iguanas. Biology and Conservation. Univ. California Press, Berkeley. xvi + 356 pp.

McBirney, A. R., and M. N. Bass. 1969. Geology of Bay Islands, Gulf of Honduras. Mem. Amer. Assoc. Petrol. Geol. 11:229–243.

McCranie, J. R. 2004. Geographic distribution. *Rhadinaea decorata*. Herpetol. Rev. 35(3):294.

_____. In prep. The Reptiles of Honduras.

_____, and F. E. Castañeda. 2004. A new species of snake of the genus *Omoadiphas* (Reptilia: Colubridae) from the Cordillera Nombre de Dios in northern Honduras. Proc. Biol. Soc. Washington 117(3):311–316.

_____, M. R. Espinal, and L. D. Wilson. 2005. A new species of montane salamander of the *Bolitoglossa dunni* group from northern Comayagua, Honduras (Urodela: Plethodontidae). Jour. Herpetol. 39(1):108–112.

_____, and G. Köhler. 1999. Two new species of colubrid snakes of the genus *Enulius* from Islas de la Bahía, Honduras. Carib. Jour. Sci. 35(1–2):14–22.

_____, K. E. Nicholson, and F. E. Castañeda. 2002. Geographic distribution. *Eleutherodactylus diastema*. Herpetol. Rev. 33(3):220.

_____, J. H. Townsend, and L. D. Wilson. 2003a. *Hyla miliaria* (Anura: Hylidae) in Honduras, with notes on calling site. Carib. Jour. Sci. 39(3):398–399

_____, _____, and _____. 2003b. Three snakes new to the herpetofauna of Honduras. Herpetol. Rev. 34(4):391–392.

_____, _____, and _____. In prep. The Amphibians and Reptiles of the Mosquitia, Honduras.

_____, and L. D. Wilson. 2002. The amphibians of Honduras. Soc. Study Amphib. Reptiles, Contrib. Herpetol. 19:i–x, 1–625.

_____, _____, and K. L. Williams. 1993. New species of tree frog of the genus *Hyla* (Anura: Hylidae) from northern Honduras. Copeia 1993(4):1057–1062.

McDiarmid, R. W., J. A. Campbell, and T. A. Touré. 1999. Snake Species of the World. A Taxonomic and Geographic Reference. Volume 1. The Herpetologists' League, Washington. xi + 511 pp.

Morgan, J. G., and M. E. B. Carter. 2002. Investigating Biology. Fourth edition. Benjamin Cummings, San Francisco, California. xxiv + 776 pp.

Ogden, J. C., and N. B. Ogden. 1998. Reconnaissance survey of the coral reefs and associated ecosystems of Cayos Cochinos, Honduras. Rev. Biol. Trop. 46(Suppl. 4):67–74.

Parker, H. W. 1940. Undescribed anatomical structures and new species of reptiles and amphibians. Ann. Mag. Nat. Hist., (11) 5:257–274.

Pellegrino, K. C. M., M. T. Rodrigues, Y. Yonenaga-Yassuda, and J. W. Sites, Jr. 2001. A molecular perspective on the evolution of microteiid lizards (Squamata, Gymnophthalmidae), and a new classification of the family. Biol. Jour. Linnaean Soc. 74:315–338.

Peters, J. A. 1964. Dictionary of Herpetology. A Brief and Meaningful Definition of Words and Terms used in Herpetology. Hafner Publ. Co., New York. vii + 392 pp.

Peters, W. 1863. Über einen Neuen Gecko, *Brachydactylis mitratus* aus Costa Rica. Monatsber. Königl. Preuss. Akad. Wissensch. Berlin 1863:41–44.

Pinet, P. R. 1975. Structural evolution of the Honduras continental margin and the sea floor south of the western Cayman Trough. Geol. Soc. Amer. Bull. 86:830–838.

Pough, F. H., R. M. Andrews, J. E. Cadle, M. L. Crump. A. H. Savitzky, and K. D. Wells. 2003 (2004). Herpetology. Third Edition. Pearson Prentice Hall, Upper Saddle River, New Jersey. ix + 726 pp.

Price, R. M., and P. Russo. 1991. Revisionary comments on the genus *Boa* with the description of a new subspecies of *Boa constrictor* from Peru. Snake 23:29–35.

Primack, R. B. 1998. Essentials of Conservation Biology. Second Edition. Sinauer Associates, Sunderland, Massachusetts. xii + 659 pp.

Raven, P. H., and L. R. Berg. 2001. Environment. Third edition. Harcourt College Publishers, Fort Worth, Texas. xxx + 612 pp.

Reeder, T. W., C. J. Cole, and H. C. Dessauer. 2002. Phylogenetic relationships of whiptail lizards of the genus *Cnemidophorus* (Squamata: Teiidae): a test of monophyly, reevaluation of karyotypic evolution, and review of hybrid origins. Amer. Mus. Novitates 3365:1–61.

Rösler, H. 2000. Kommentierte Liste der rezenten, subrezenten und fossilen Gecko-Taxa (Reptilia: Gekkonomorpha). Gekkota 2:28–153.

Roughgarden, J. 1995. *Anolis* lizards of the Caribbean: Ecology, Evolution, and Plate Tectonics. Oxford Univ. Press, New York. xi + 200 pp.

Russell, A. P., and A. M. Bauer. 2002. *Thecadactylus, T. rapicauda*. Cat. Amer. Amphib. Reptiles 753:1–16.

Sagra, R. de la. 1839–1843. Historia Fisca, Politica y Natural de la Isla de Cuba. Segunda Parte. Historia Natural. Tomo IV. Reptiles y Peces. Arthus Bertrand, Paris. 143 p (reptiles only).

Sauer, C. O. 1966. The Early Spanish Main. Univ. of California Press, Berkeley. xii + 306 pp.

Savage, J. M. 1987. Systematics and distribution of the Mexican and Central American rainfrogs of the *Eleutherodactylus gollmeri* group (Amphibia: Leptodactylidae). Fieldiana: Zool., New Series 33:i–iv, 1–57.

_____. 2002. The Amphibians and Reptiles of Costa Rica. A Herpetofauna between Two Continents, between Two Seas. Univ. Chicago Press, Chicago, Illinois. xx + 934 pp.

Schulte, J. A., II., J. P. Valladares, and A. Larson. 2003. Phylogenetic relationships within Iguanidae inferred using molecular and morphological data and a phylogenetic taxonomy of iguanian lizards. Herpetologica 59(3):399–419.

Seidel, M. E. 2002. Taxonomic observations on extant species and subspecies of slider turtles, genus *Trachemys*. Jour. Herpetol. 36(2):285–292.

Smith, H. M., and K. L. Williams. 1966a. The ratsnake of the Bay Islands, Honduras. Nat. Hist. Misc. 185:1–2.

_____, and _____. 1966b. A new snake (*Tantilla*) from Las Islas de la Bahia, Honduras. Southwest. Nat. 11(4):483–487.

Squier, E. G. 1855. Notes on Central America, particularly the states of Honduras and San Salvador. Harper and Roberts, New York. 397 pp.

Stafford, P. J., and J. R. Meyer. "2000" (1999). A Guide to the Reptiles of Belize. Nat. Hist. Mus. London. xix + 356 pp.

Stejneger, L. 1901. On a new species of spiny-tailed iguana from Utilla Island, Honduras. Proc. U.S. Natl. Mus. 23:467–468.

Stonich, S. C. 2000. The Other Side of Paradise: Tourism, Conservation, and Development in the Bay Islands. Cognizant Communication Corporation, New York. xiii + 205 pp.

Taylor, E. H. 1940. Herpetological miscellany, no. I. Univ. Kansas Sci. Bull. 26:489–571.

Villa, J. 1969. Two new insular subspecies of the natricid snake *Tretanorhinus nigroluteus* Cope from Honduras and Nicaragua. Jour. Herpetol. 3(3–4):145–150.

_____, and J. R. McCranie. 1995. *Oxybelis wilsoni*, a new species of vine snake from Isla de Roatán, Honduras (Serpentes: Colubridae). Rev. Biol. Trop. 43(1–3):297–305.

Wagler, J. 1824. Serpentum Brasiliensium Species Novae ou Histoire Naturelle des Espècies Nouvelles de Serpens, Recueillies et Observées Pendant le Voyage dans l'Intérieur du Brésil dans les Années 1817, 1818, 1819, 1820, Exécuté par Orde de sa Majesté le Roi de Baviére. Franc. Seraph. Hübschmanni. Monachii. viii + 74 pp.

Weyl, R. 1980. Geology of Central America, Second, Completely Revised Edition. Gebrüder Borntraeger, Berlin. viii + 371 pp.

Wiegmann, A. F. A. 1828. Behträge zur Amphibienkunde. Isis von Oken 21(III–IV):cols. 364–383.

Wilson, E. O. 2002. The Future of Life. Alfred A. Knopf, New York. xxiv + 229 pp.

Wilson, L. D. 1999. Checklist and key to the species of the genus *Tantilla* (Serpentes: Colubridae), with some commentary on distribution. Smithsonian Herpetol. Info. Serv. 122:1–34.

_____, and G. A. Cruz Díaz. 1993. The herpetofauna of the Cayos Cochinos, Honduras. Herpetol. Nat. Hist. 1(1):13–23.

_____, and D. E. Hahn. 1973. The herpetofauna of the Islas de la Bahía, Honduras. Bull. Florida State Mus. Biol. Ser. 17(2):93–150.

_____, and J. R. McCranie. 1999. The systematic status of Honduran populations of the *Tantilla taeniata* group (Serpentes: Colubridae), with notes on other populations. Amphibia-Reptilia 20(3):326–329.

_____, and _____. 2002. Update on the list of reptiles known from Honduras. Herpetol. Rev. 33(2):90–94.

_____, and _____. 2003. Herpetofaunal indicator species as measures of environmental stability in Honduras. Caribbean Jour. Sci. 39(1):50–67.

_____, and _____. 2004. The conservation status of the herpetofauna of Honduras. Amphibian and Reptile Conservation. 3(1):6–33.

_____, _____, and M. R. Espinal. 2001. The ecogeography of the Honduran herpetofauna and the design of biotic reserves, pp. 109–158. *In* J. D. Johnson, R. G. Webb, and O. A. Flores-Villela (Eds.), Mesoamerican herpetology: systematics, zoogeography, and conservation. Centennial Museum, Univ. Texas El Paso, Spec. Publ. 1:i–iv, 1–200.

_____, _____, S. Gotte, and J. H. Townsend. 2003. Distributional comments on some members of the herpetofauna of the Mosquitia, Honduras. Herpetol. Bull. 84:15–19.

_____, and J. R. Meyer. 1985. The Snakes of Honduras. Second Edition. Milwaukee Pub. Mus., Milwaukee, Wisconsin. x + 150 pp.

Wright, R. 1994. The Moral Animal: The New Science of Evolutionary Psychology. Pantheon Books, New York. x + 467 pp.

Zhao, E.-M., and K. Adler. 1993. Herpetology of China. Soc. Study Amphib. Reptiles, Contrib. Herpetol. 10:1–522.

Index to Scientific Names

Page numbers in bold face refer to the species accounts. Citations in light face represent entries in other text; when a number is followed by the letters F, P, or T, those letters refer to figures, photographs, or entries in a table, respectively. Only scientific names of amphibians and reptiles are entered alphabetically both by the generic and specific names.

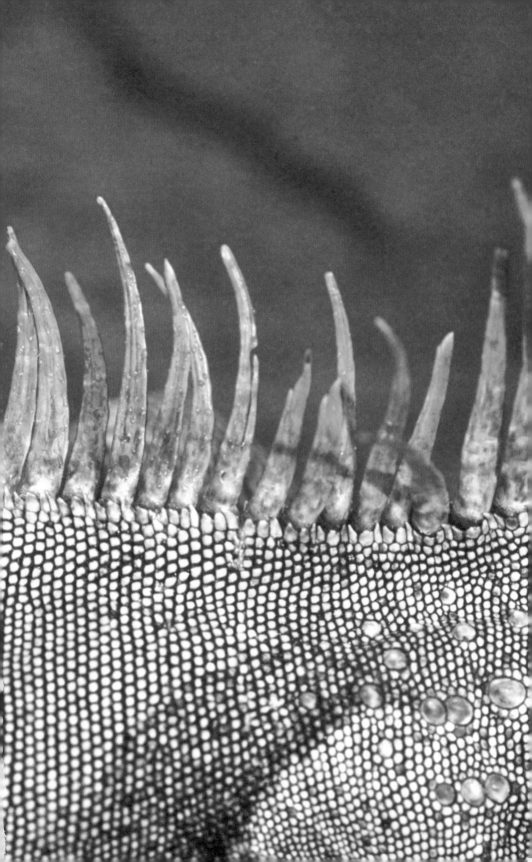